I MAY BE WRONG

I MAY BE WRONG

BJÖRN NATTHIKO LINDEBLAD
CAROLINE BANKLER
& NAVID MODIRI

Translated from the Swedish by
Agnes Broome

BLOOMSBURY PUBLISHING
LONDON • OXFORD • NEW YORK • NEW DELHI • SYDNEY

BLOOMSBURY PUBLISHING
Bloomsbury Publishing Plc
50 Bedford Square, London, WC1B 3DP, UK
29 Earlsfort Terrace, Dublin 2, Ireland

BLOOMSBURY, BLOOMSBURY PUBLISHING and the Diana logo are
trademarks of Bloomsbury Publishing Plc

First published in 2020 in Sweden as *Jag kan ha fel* by Bonnier Fakta
First published in Great Britain 2022

Published by agreement with Salomonsson Agency
Björn Natthiko Lindeblad has asserted his right under the Copyright, Designs and
Patents Act, 1988, to be identified as Author of this work

This advance reading copy is printed from uncorrected proof pages. This does not
represent the final text and should not be quoted without reference to the final
printed book

A catalogue record for this book is available from the British Library

ISBN: HB: 978-1-5266-4482-4; TPB: 978-1-5266-4481-7;
eBook: 978-1-5266-4480-0; EPDF: 978-1-5266-4479-4

2 4 6 8 10 9 7 5 3 1

Typeset by Newgen KnowledgeWorks Pvt. Ltd., Chennai, India
Printed and bound in Great Britain by CPI Group (UK) Ltd, Croydon CR0 4YY

To find out more about our authors and books visit www.bloomsbury.com and sign
up for our newsletters

Contents

CONTENTS

Prologue

After leaving my life as a monk behind and returning to Sweden, I was interviewed by a newspaper. They wanted to know more about my somewhat unusual life choices. Why would a successful businessman give away everything he owns, shave his head and go off into the jungle to live with a bunch of strangers? Some way into our conversation, the interviewer asked the million-dollar question:

'What is the most important thing you learned during your seventeen years as a Buddhist forest monk?'

The question made me feel nervous and flustered. I had to say something, but I didn't want to rush this particular answer.

The journalist sitting across from me wasn't a person of any discernible spiritual interest. He had no doubt been shocked to learn about all the things I'd chosen to forego during my time as a monk. After all, I'd lived without money, without sex or masturbation, without TV or novels, without alcohol, without family, without holidays, without modern conveniences, without choosing when or what to eat.

For seventeen years.

Of my own free will.

And so, what did I get out of it?

It was important to me to be honest. I wanted my response to be the absolute truth as I saw it. So, I looked inward and before long the answer bubbled up from some quiet place inside:

What I value most from my seventeen years of full-time spiritual training is that I no longer believe my every thought.

That's my superpower.

What's great about that is that it's everyone's super-power. Yours, too. If you've lost sight of it, I hope I can help to guide you along the path to rediscovering it.

It's a tremendous privilege to have had so many opportunities to share what I learned during my years of continual effort to achieve spiritual and personal growth. I've always found those opportunities deeply meaningful. I've been given so many things that have helped me, that have made my life easier to live, made it easier to be me. If I'm lucky, you will find something in this book that can help you. Some of these insights have been pivotal to me. Not least in the past two years, when I've found myself in Death's waiting room earlier than I would have wished. Perhaps this is where it ends. But perhaps it's also where it begins.

ONE

Awareness

I'm eight years old. As usual, I'm the first to wake. I pace around my grandparents' house on an island on the outskirts of Karlskrona, south-east Sweden, waiting for my younger brother Nils to wake up. I pause at the kitchen window. Suddenly, the noise inside me falls silent.

Everything goes quiet. The chrome toaster on the windowsill is so beautiful I skip a breath. Time stops. Everything seems to shimmer. A couple of clouds smile down from a pale morning sky. The birch tree outside the window waves its glittering leaves. Everywhere I look, I see beauty.

I probably didn't put my experience into words back then, but I would like to try to now. It was as though the world was whispering: '*Welcome home.*' For the first time, I felt completely at home on this planet. I was present in the here and now, with no thoughts. Then my eyes welled up and I felt a warmth in my chest, which today I would call *gratitude*. Hard on its heels followed the hope that this feeling would last forever, or at least for a really long time. It didn't, of course. But I've never forgotten that morning

I have never felt completely comfortable with the term *mindfulness*. My mind doesn't feel full when I'm truly in the moment. More like a big, empty, welcoming space, with plenty of room for everyone and everything. Conscious presence. It sounds like hard work, the opposite of being relaxed. For that reason, I like to use a different word: *awareness*.

We become aware, we remain aware, we are aware. It was *awareness* that blossomed that early morning beside the toaster in Karlskrona. It feels like leaning into something soft. The thoughts, the feelings, the physical sensations – everything is allowed to be *exactly as it is*. It makes us a little bit bigger. We notice things in and around ourselves we haven't noticed before. It's an intimate feeling. Like an invisible friend whose always on your side.

Needless to say, your degree of presence affects how you relate to other people. We all know what it's like to spend time with someone who isn't present. There's always this nagging sense that something's missing. I feel it comes to the fore every time I meet young children. They're less than impressed by our analytical skills, but amazingly sensitive as to whether or not we are in the moment. They can tell when we're faking or when our thoughts are somewhere else. The same goes for animals.

But when we're present, when we're not hypnotised by every little thought that flashes into our heads, people find us much more pleasant to be around. They give us their trust. They give us their attention. We connect with the world around us in a completely different way. You know this already, of course, and it may sound trite. And yet, many of us forget. It's so easy to become hung up on appearing clever and impressive that we forget just how far sincerity can take us.

TWO

Successful but unfulfilled

I left school with good grades and had my pick of universities, but no clear plan for my future. Taking a fairly casual approach to the whole thing, I applied to a few different degree courses. As it happened, I was in Stockholm that August when the entrance exams for the Stockholm School of Economics were being held. It was the path my dad had chosen: finance, economics, big companies. So I sat the exams, an entire day of demanding tests. Turns out I did well and a few months later I received a letter saying I had got in. Lacking in direction as I was, I reckoned I had nothing to lose by enrolling. Economics is always useful; it opens lots of doors. So I'd been told. But the real reason I decided to accept my offer from the Stockholm School of Economics was probably that it made my dad proud.

I graduated in the spring of 1985. I was twenty-three. Sweden's labour market was booming. Employers recruited us straight out of school, before we had even graduated. One sunny evening in May, I was sitting in a fancy restaurant on Strandvägen in central Stockholm with an older investment banker. I was being interviewed for a potential job over dinner. I did my best to sound intelligent and eat at the same time, always something of a challenge for me. When the dinner and interview were over, we shook hands and the banker said:

'Look, I'm pretty sure you're going to be asked to go to our head office in London for further interviews. But can I give you a piece of advice before you go?'

'Please.'

'When you get to the next interview stage with my London colleagues, try to appear a bit more interested in the work.'

I knew what he meant, of course, but I was taken aback at being called out. Back then, I was, like so many of my peers, a young person in search of my adult life. That often means working with what you've got. Sometimes, there's an element of playacting involved, like pretending you're more interested in something than you really are. On that particular evening, my acting skills failed to convince. But things seemed to work out anyway. I had other job offers and, before long, I was climbing that career ladder.

A couple of years later, one Sunday afternoon in May, I was lying on an scratchy red Ikea sofa I'd had shipped over from Sweden, a warm sea breeze sifting in through the open window. I was working for a big international company and had been transferred to their Spanish offices. I had a company car. A secretary. Flew business class. Had a lovely house by the sea. In another two months, I was set to become the youngest ever chief financial officer of an AGA subsidiary. I'd been featured in the AGA in-house magazine and was unquestionably outwardly successful. I was only twenty-six years old and, to an outsider, my life was the picture of perfection. But I think almost everyone who has ever appeared outwardly successful has also eventually realised that's no guarantee of happiness.

Success and happiness are two different things.

To others, it must have seemed I'd played my cards right. I had all the trappings of material and professional success. I'd gone straight from university to three intense work years in half a dozen countries. But I'd done it with sheer willpower and self-discipline. I was still playing a part, still pretending to be interested in economics. You can get away with that for so long. But we all know there comes a day when discipline alone is no longer enough. A job, what we spend our days doing, has to nourish and stimulate some deeper part of our being. That type of nourishment is rarely derived from success. Rather, it comes from feeling connected to the people you work with, feeling that your work has meaning, that your talents are somehow making a difference.

Me? I felt a bit like I was playing dress-up when I put on my suit and picked up my shiny, square briefcase to go to work. I would tie my tie in front of the mirror in the mornings, give myself a thumbs up and tell my reflection: 'It's showtime, folks!' But my internal, subjective experience was: 'I don't feel good. I don't like going to work. Thinking about work often makes me anxious. There's a twenty-four-seven swirl of doubts at the back of my mind, with questions like "Did I do enough prep? Am I good enough? When are they going to see through me? When are they going to realise I'm just pretending to be interested in economics?"'

As I lay there on my red sofa, those doubts seemed more insistent than usual. I thought about what the books at the Stockholm School of Economics had taught me: what is the prime motivation of an economist working for a big company? Maximising the profits of the shareholder. What does that mean for me? Who are they? Have I ever even met a shareholder? (And even if I have, why would I be interested in maximising their profits?)

My mind was buzzing with thoughts about the coming work week and my to-do list. There were some things I needed to get done but didn't feel fully up to doing. A management meeting where I was expected to have an opinion about whether or not a carbonic acid plant outside Madrid should be expanded. A quarterly report I had to submit to our headquarters in Sweden. In other words, my chest was contracting with plain old Sunday night angst. I assume just about everyone knows what that's like. When you're in that kind of mental state, it's as though your every thought passes through a dark filter. Whatever you're thinking about, it leads to worry, anxiety, despondency, helplessness. I remember thinking something along the lines of: '*How can I help myself? I'm lying here, stuck in a spiral of dark thoughts. This isn't good for me.*'

Then I recalled a book I'd recently read. For the third time, as a matter of fact. I found it pretty dense, so even though I'd read it cover to cover three times I reckoned I'd only understood about thirty to forty per cent of the material. The book was called *Zen and the Art of Motorcycle Maintenance*.

It wasn't really so much about Zen Buddhism. Or the art of motorcycle maintenance, for that matter. But it did contain a lot of ideas. And one of the ideas I picked up on was: 'That which is peaceful inside us humans, that which is still and calm, that isn't ruffled by thoughts that are always present in the background – that is valuable, that is worth taking note of. That has rewards.'

After a while, I had a dawning sense of realisation. '*Okay, so, all the thoughts I'm thinking right now are making me feel bad. Just blocking them seems impossible. Swapping them for positive ones feels disingenuous. I mean, am I supposed to lie here and pretend I'm looking forward to that management meeting?! Talk about superficial. What can I do if I want to achieve calm and stop being hypnotised by my own thoughts?*'

The book underscored the value of locating the stillness we all have inside. But how was I supposed to do that? Practically speaking, how was I supposed to turn towards my inner tranquillity? While it wasn't immediately obvious to me how to go about it, the concept did appeal to me.

I'd heard one way of getting there might be through meditation. But I knew very little about what meditation really entailed. It seemed to have a lot to do with *breathing* – people who meditated seemed very focused on their breathing. That couldn't be all that hard, could it? As far as I could remember I'd been breathing since the moment I was born. But I also realised, of course, that people who meditated seemed to *engage* with their breathing, to *observe* it, in a way I didn't. I could certainly give it a go, though. It was worth a shot.

So, like the novice I was, I started trying to track my breathing. 'That's the start of the inhalation. That's where it ends. That's where exhalation starts. That's where that ends. Short pause.'

I'm not saying it was easy, or that it came particularly naturally to me. It was a constant struggle to maintain my focus and stop my mind from wandering. But I kept at it for ten to fifteen minutes, patiently shepherding my mind back to my breathing, again and again, while my thoughts kept bolting off towards 'What should I say in that management meeting?' Or 'Should I make gazpacho for dinner again?' Or 'When can I next go back to Sweden?' Or 'Why did my girlfriend break up with me?'

Eventually, though, things slowed down a little. Not in a remarkable, religious or mystical way, just in the way that things do tend to slow down during the calmer periods of a person's week or month. It was enough to allow me to create some critical distance from the torrent of thoughts, rather than just frantically trying to keep my head above water. The pressure in my chest eased a little. The breaks between the anxious thoughts grew slightly longer. The feeling of just existing became a little bit more accessible. And within this relative calm, from a fairly still place within me, a quiet thought surfaced. I probably wouldn't even call it a thought; it was more of an impulse. Something inside me, that seemed to come out of nowhere, that wasn't the final link in a chain of thoughts, that wasn't the result of reasoning, but that, rather, just suddenly appeared. It stood there before me, clear and fully formed:

It's time to move on.

It took me about five seconds to make my mind up. Just allowing myself to think about quitting my job and walking away from everything was extremely refreshing. The idea felt both dangerous and dynamic. My body was filled with a fizzing energy that washed over me in waves. I had to get up and dance it out. (Right then, I imagine I looked a bit like Baloo the bear.) I felt so powerful and proactive. It might have been the first decision I ever made all by myself, without anxiously glancing over my shoulder, wondering what people would think.

A couple of days later I handed in my notice.

THREE

Breathe more, think less

My attempt to meditate for fifteen minutes as a desperate twenty-six-year-old in Spain would come to mean more to me than I could ever have dreamed at the time. At that moment I was just looking for a way to handle my immediate lack of wellbeing, but the effort left me wanting more. I wanted to hear what that wise voice inside me had to say.

It's not that I had some sort of grand awakening the moment I thought about starting to listen to my inner voice, or that I achieved some unique mental state. But the brief reprieve from my wildly spinning thoughts gave me a wonderful sense of freedom. They weren't gone, but they weren't quite so hypnotic anymore. It was as though I'd taken a step back mentally and started to realise that while I *have* thoughts, I am not my thoughts.

Thoughts are not a problem in and of themselves, of course. But automatically, uncritically identifying with every passing thought – that's a huge problem. The untrained mind often does this. We feel that our identity and our thoughts are inextricably linked.

I'm not here to encourage positive thinking. Absolutely not. Personally, I'm not convinced positive thinking is very powerful. I've always found it to be relatively superficial.

What about trying not to think at all, then? Good luck with that one. I would go so far as to say that's pretty much physically impossible. Try not to think about a pink elephant. Our brain is unable to comprehend the word 'not'. But learning how to let go of a thought – that can be endlessly helpful.

So how do you let go of a train of thought that's dragging you along with it? You turn your attention elsewhere. The only thing fuelling your thoughts is your attention.

Imagine a fist unclenching into an open hand – it shows us how we can let go of things and thoughts and let them fly. That simple gesture, of briefly letting go of what we're thinking about, goes a long way. Deliberately and consciously directing our attention towards something less complicated, such as a physical experience like breathing, can constitute a healing, soothing break from our inner chaos.

Maybe it can help you, too, if you're willing to try it?

*

When it's time to breathe in, imagine a rising within your body. As if your upper body is a bottle of water. When we exhale, the water level sinks, the bottle empties, and when we inhale, it rises back up, from the bottom. Imagine your breath starting from your hips, or all the way down by the floor. Then the water level rises through your stomach, chest and neck.

See if you can just let these two waves anchor you for a while — the falling wave on the exhale and the rising wave on the inhale. If you have to adjust, do it kindly, gently, as though asking your body: how does breathing work best for you? Is it easier for you to take in air if I open up a bit more in the chest? Drop my shoulders slightly? Find the part of you that thinks it's good enough. That feels good.

This breathing, that's all you have to do for the moment. You're taking a break from everything else. Your frontal lobe has switched off. In this moment, you have no responsibilities. In this moment, there's no plan to formulate, no opinion to give, nothing to remember. The only thing you need to do is breathe. Stay with it for as long as you feel like it.

How often do you give yourself this kind of attention? Don't be afraid to seize the opportunity when it presents itself. Not because you're hoping to get something out of it. Not to make every part of your life calm and peaceful. Not in the hope of experiencing internal fireworks. Not because you want to be a more spiritual person. Just because the breathing itself is worth it.

Think about all the big words associated with breathing. Another word for breathing is aspiration. Spirit, spiritual. There's something there. If you want to access more of your vitality, get used to paying attention to your breathing.

Thai monk Ajahn Chah, a master in the Buddhist tradition I joined, once said: 'There are people who are born and die and never once are aware of their breath going in and out of their body. That's how far away from themselves they live.'

Choosing where to direct your attention may sound easy, but I'll be the first to admit how extremely difficult it can be. When we first start to try to focus on our breathing, most of our minds behave like frantic yoyos. You follow along for a handful of breaths, then your attention wanders off to something trivial and you patiently have to reel it back in. Again and again and again. Our minds are virtually inexhaustible when it comes to darting off in the most unexpected directions. But every time our focus slips, we eventually notice. All we can do then is to note that it happened (again) without scolding ourselves or assessing our level of success, let go of those thoughts and calmly steer our attention back to the intended object.

It's tempting to quit. But it's worth hanging in there. Because even though this is just a small, unspectacular gesture in your own individual life, it's also an entirely necessary and invaluable step in the evolution of our collective human awareness.

The value of stillness and of inward listening has been emphasised and underscored in all religions since time immemorial. It goes beyond Buddhism and meditation and prayer rituals. It has to do with being human.

We all have the ability to let go of our thoughts, to choose *where* we direct our attention, *how long* we allow our attention to linger on things that cause us harm. You do, too. Sometimes, you just need a bit of practice. Because when we ignore or completely lose interest in that ability, we end up at the mercy of ingrained, automated behaviours, views and patterns. They have us on a lead, so to speak. And so we keep trudging round and round the same track. That's not freedom. That's not dignity.

Is this easy?

No.

Is it still worth doing the best you can, at your own pace?

Yes.

FOUR

The Brothers Karamazov

It wasn't entirely easy knocking on my boss's door and suddenly saying: 'Look, things aren't working out as we planned. I'm quitting.' Nor was it easy to call Mum and Dad: 'Yes, I quit my job. No, I don't have a plan B.'

A month after resigning, I was back home in Gothenburg. I rented a simple studio flat – sublet it, actually – in a working-class part of town called Majorna and found a job washing dishes in a restaurant. I remember my first day, standing there with the dirty dishes, hearing the rest of the staff bantering with each other: 'Hey, there's a new dishwasher, right? Does this one speak Swedish?' Inside, my pride was screaming: '*I was actually a fairly important person until recently.*'

Shortly afterwards, I started studying literature. One morning, on the tram to the campus, I saw an ad for a newly opened mental health helpline. The idea of volunteering resonated with me, so I signed up. I was trained over the course of six Sundays and then assigned four-hour phone shifts on Thursday nights. At first, I was eager to give advice. But then, gradually, I learned just to be still and listen with an open heart.

For the first time, I was faced with the less rosy side of my hometown. Loneliness and hardship. Despair and helplessness. I often didn't want to go to my shifts. But afterwards, I always felt a few inches taller, with warmth and purpose singing in my chest. As often as people cried about their lives, they cried with gratitude because someone was finally listening to them. For some, it had been decades since anyone had given them that kind of attention. I was reminded of something important: being there for others is infinitely rewarding.

After a year of studying literature, I broadened my search to the wider world. Eventually, I ended up in India, working as an economist for the United Nation's World Food Programme. It was a classic example of young, idealistic, starry-eyed westerner come to help India. The end result: India helps young, idealistic, starry-eyed westerner much more. During my year there, I also backpacked around Southeast Asia. For three weeks I walked up and down the mountains of the Himalayas. It was incredible. Ever since I was little, I've loved the mountains unconditionally. They've always been my favourite environment, my element. Being among high peaks makes me happy almost by default. So you can probably imagine how good

I was feeling, walking ridiculously far every day through the magnificent massifs.

I imagine anyone who has ever undertaken a longer trek knows what it feels like after a while; somehow, the complexity of life is reduced day by day. Eventually, it boils down to the weather, your body, food, drink and rest. I remember putting on my backpack in the morning and feeling I could walk to the ends of the earth – this is all I want to do. I felt invincible.

That being said, I might have been the least intelligent packer in history. I strongly suspect I was the only hiker that year pretentious enough to lug around a heavy hardback copy of Dostoevsky's The Brothers Karamazov, a tome I was invariably far too tired to read once I'd made camp at night.

At the end of my almost month-long trek, I returned to the Nepalese capital Kathmandu, a popular stop-off for backpackers. I'd eaten the same food for weeks – lentil stew with rice, three times a day – so I enthusiastically ordered a sumptuous breakfast at a place that supposedly served the best croissants in town. A very beautiful, rebellious medical student from Cape Town sat down across from me.

She told me her name was Hailey.

All my life I've had a complex about my poor flirting skills. I must have overslept the day God handed out the

Big Book of Flirting. But apparently I did something right that morning. Breakfast ended up lasting four hours and before it was over I was convinced I was in love with the loud, colourful and slightly rowdy woman sitting in front of me. And what's more, the feeling was mutual. A few days later, we travelled on to Thailand together and for a few weeks we enjoyed an immaculate, almost cinematic beach romance. Then she dumped me.

I think what happened after the first two, dreamlike, weeks was that I started worrying that I might like her more than she liked me. It was a short leap from there to a bigger fear:

What if she leaves me?

Those doubts closed off something within me. It happened quickly. I'm guessing that same mechanism is also what caused my emotions to start shutting down. And when you're closed off emotionally, playfulness, lightness, humour and spontaneity are all out of reach. You become mute and rigid. I certainly did. I also kept telling myself I *shouldn't* be so mute or rigid, which made me even *more* mute and rigid. When Hailey eventually, very gently and considerately, confirmed my fears by breaking up with me, all I could think of saying was: 'You know what, if I was with someone like me, the way I am right now, I'd break up with me, too.'

I was old enough to have been dumped a few times before, but that did nothing to cushion the blow. I know

22

now I'm not the only one who feels the pain of rejection extra keenly. Often, those are people's deepest wounds. To make things worse, I've always been a bit of a drama queen.

So, there I was, newly dumped on a beach in Thailand. Lonelier than ever and utterly heartbroken. It was a classic backpacker spot. Everywhere I looked I saw carefree, beautiful, tanned, playful, adventurous, outgoing, young people.

And then there was me. Hiding behind my well-worn copy of Dostoevsky, trying to look deep, as if all I needed in life was the universe of grand ideas. I kept it up for a few days. Then it became glaringly obvious that I was just deeply depressed.

It was painfully clear to me I had no idea how to handle feeling that bad. Really no idea at all. I had no tools whatsoever. And I couldn't help but think: 'Isn't that a bit odd? Sixteen years of education, and I don't remember a single lesson where I learned anything on the theme of "What do you do when life gets hard?"'

We all need guidance from time to time. I can't imagine a person whose life is never hard. We all go through periods when we feel utterly lonely, helpless, friendless, misunderstood, ill-treated. And when a storm is brewing, we need to find things to hold onto, lash ourselves to. We can find them outside ourselves or within. Preferably both.

This is the part of the story when we get to what I know sounds trite, a cliché: young, heartbroken man finds his way to a monastery.

But that's exactly what happened. I'd never really taken much of an interest in religion, but it had become so painfully obvious I was helpless in dealing with the kinds of powerful emotions I was overcome with back then. I needed to do something. It was time to ask for help and the Buddha seemed a good place to start.

FIVE

My monastery debut

I'd been given the address of a monastery in northern Thailand that offered month-long meditation courses in English. Even though I'd dabbled in meditation before, I still had only the vaguest idea of what it was really about. But I'd seen Buddhist monks during my travels, and they seemed pretty relaxed and content to me, ambling about at dawn with their alms bowls, collecting food from the locals. What's more, there was something about the Thai people in general that fascinated me. They were comfortable in their own skins somehow. There was something grounded about them that I hadn't come across as much in the West.

Ever since I was little, I'd had a voice inside me whispering I wasn't good enough. A voice that grew a lot louder whenever I did something awkward or stupid, like if I misunderstood something or failed. And fell silent whenever I did something good. Even back then,

I realised it wasn't a unique problem, that it was part of my cultural heritage. A lot of people in our part of the world live with the continual grumblings of a harsh inner critic. A voice that's ungenerous when it speaks to us, even when we've done nothing worse than make an innocent mistake. We often carry around a feeling of not measuring up, a fear of being 'found out'. We doubt people would like us if they knew what we were really like. We play games to make sure they don't. Those kinds of things necessarily affect the way we interact with the world around us. That became particularly obvious when contrasted with the Thais I met.

The Thai people seemed, simply put, to like themselves much more. Rarely have I met a westerner who radiated the same kind of genuine certainty that the world will welcome them as they are. I felt like any Thai would be able to walk into a room and with an astonishing confidence exude something along the lines of: 'Hi, I'm here! Great, isn't it? Isn't everything better when I'm around?! I'm assuming everyone thinks it's fantastic that I'm here and I'm convinced you all like me!' A slightly facetious and exaggerated description perhaps, but that was pretty much my impression. And I liked it.

I arrived at the monastery I'd been told about with outrageously outsized expectations about what meditation has to offer. It was a small, busy village monastery near the airport outside Chiang Mai. We were surrounded by flea-ridden dogs that ate our spicy leftovers and it was raucous and loud. For some reason, the monastery was fond of a kind of folk music festival. Sometimes electronic music was playing and young people were dancing on a stage right outside while we were supposed to meditate.

It seemed to me the monks spent most of their time smoking and gossiping. It was us westerners who meditated. But we were, on the other hand, incredibly earnest about it.

A relatively accurate description of what my thoughts were like while I meditated on the second day of the course might go something like this:

Okay, let's go. Forty-five minutes of unbroken mindfulness. Breathing is the way forward. I'm going to leave my despair behind in this place and emerge as a new man. Maybe I can even win Hailey back? Inhale, exhale, I wonder what's for lunch today? That stuff they served yesterday wouldn't be fit for a dog back home. And meanwhile, all around here, the trees are heavy with sun-ripened, exotic fruit... All right, focus. Inhale, exhale. But seriously, the coffee in this place? It's ridiculous! As far as I can see, we, the western backpackers, are basically bankrolling this place. We're filling their donation boxes. And we're not okay with Nescafé! They would have made their money back in no time if they'd invested in a proper, Italian coffeemaker. Cortado, cappuccino... Whoa, what just happened? I was supposed to be meditating, reaching a higher plane. Instead, my attention was hijacked by these bizarrely

27

impassioned thoughts. Since when is it my job to pimp the monastery menu? Good thing no one heard. I'm meant to be one of the
serious ones. Get it together. Go back to focusing on your breathing.
Feel your body. Let go. The Buddha was big on letting go. Let's get
to it. Inhale, exhale... Seriously, this is so boring! Isn't something
supposed to happen? This can't be it. How long until I get to the
cosmic orgasm? The internal fireworks? I'm so ready!

If you've ever tried meditation, I'm sure you can
relate. You thought of yourself as a more or less reasonable, rational, sensible and pragmatic being, but then you
discovered some kind of travelling monkey circus is in
fact in charge of your thought process most of the time.
A lot of us made the same mistake when we first started
meditating; we thought our minds would go quiet. That's
not how it works! Possibly for brief moments, but no
more than that. Only dead people have quiet minds. For
as long as we're alive, we're in possession of an intellect,
and the nature of the human intellect is to generate ideas,
compare those ideas with others, reformulate them,
question them.

When faced with the insane, completely uncensored
thoughts that bounce around in our heads, it's easy to
feel both astonished and horrified. It makes you happy
other people can't read minds. We can take comfort in
the fact that it's the same for everyone. It's natural. There's
nothing weird about it. We just have to understand that

these are *thoughts* – not truths. Besides, taking note of our internal thought circus can be useful because it can help us create some distance from it when we really need to. We can learn to take our thoughts less seriously, find a more sober way of relating to them: *'What do you know, there's that ridiculous thought again. Oh well. I'm not going to hold onto that one.'*

One of the reasons I like being with people who have begun their inward journey is that they've just discovered the chaos in their brains and have therefore created some distance between themselves and their thoughts. Inevitably, this makes them humbler. And it's refreshing to be with people who don't take themselves and their convictions so seriously all the time. Instead, we can be united in our shared realisation: *I haven't entirely got it together. You haven't entirely got it together. I'm not one hundred per cent rational. You're not one hundred per cent rational. I involuntarily think about crazy things occasionally. So do you. I have disproportionate emotional reactions to certain things. So do you.*

Once a bit of distance helps you get your thought processes into perspective and you come to realise other people are dealing with the same things as you, it automatically makes it easier to notice the things we humans share, rather than what divides us. Regardless of who we are, where we come from and what our history is, we tend to have a lot in common in terms of our inner workings. By admitting that and shining a light on it, we make it easier to stop pretending we're on top of everything. It makes it easier to help each other, to share, to genuinely meet. We can create complementary relationships instead of competitive ones, rejoice in not being solitary satellites. We can learn from each other without fear of failure. We can see what's wonderful about other people without taking the next, unfortunate step of whispering to ourselves that we're not as good.

SIX

Don't believe your every thought

It was a month-long meditation course, but I fled the monastery after just four days. I'm not a quitter. I know I'm not, because I got through three years of the Stockholm School of Economics without being genuinely interested in a single course they offered. I ran the Seville Marathon in 1987, in 35° heat, with just nine practice runs under my belt, wearing a thick cotton T-shirt my nipples have never forgiven me for. But in this case, I did give up.

By the evening of the fourth day, I was sitting in the centre of Chiang Mai with a bottle of wine, wondering what had gone wrong. What was so hard about this?

Sleeping on a wooden pallet was tolerable. Not speaking could be endured. Getting up really early was okay. Even not eating much, and bad food at that, was acceptable. But being left alone with my chattering, yammering, critical, judgemental, spiteful, questioning, complaining thoughts all day every day, with virtually no distractions – that was unbearable. As I tried to silence my mind, my mind fought back with a steady flow of personal attacks and self-doubt.

But something had awoken inside me. It was very clear to me I didn't want to live like that. Being unable to enjoy one's own company – that's a problem. So I made a kind of deal with myself then and there: *From now on, one of your guiding principles will be to become someone whose company you have a slightly easier time enduring. Someone slightly more comfortable in his own skin. Someone who isn't ruled by his thoughts. Who might one day even become a good friend to himself.*

At least I had an idea now of how to get there. I no longer felt completely at the mercy of external and internal circumstances I had no control over. After all, I'd discovered that when my sadness or anxiety or loneliness became overwhelming, I could choose to focus on my breathing, let my awareness rest in my body, and not unquestioningly believe all the thoughts my brain threw at me.

This was the first gift of the Buddha.

Some time passed, but I did eventually return to that same raucous little village monastery to complete the four-week course. It's the hardest thing I've ever done. I gave up three times before finishing. But Thanat, my kind Chinese teacher, just smiled gently each time I declared I was done. Then he'd give me some warm soy milk in a plastic bag and say: 'Sleep on it. You've come a long way to do this. Maybe you'll feel differently tomorrow morning.' I always did. And I was starting to understand why the Buddha spoke so much about impermanence. Nothing lasts. Not even the difficult times.

That was the second gift of the Buddha.

When I got back to Sweden, I continued to meditate, morning and evening. I felt as if I had finally been given a key to my inner space. I had a better sense of what lay within. When I was able to face what was hard, some of the resistance often vanished.

Directing our attention, choosing what we aim it at, is the best and possibly the only thing we can do when things get really hard.

That was the third gift of the Buddha.

'Don't believe your every thought.' Few things have helped me more in life. Unfortunately, that superpower, which we all possess, is often overlooked. But the fact is that approaching our own thoughts with a measure of scepticism and humour makes it infinitely easier to be you and me.

So what do you gain from not unquestioningly believing every thought that flashes through your mind?

Something as invaluable as a true and genuine inner confidant. Someone who is always on your side. When we believe everything we think, it leaves us vulnerable and defenceless. On every level. And it erodes our wisdom. In our darkest moments, the abyss may well be bottomless. It can literally torment us to death.

Where's the dignity, where's the freedom, in a life where you believe everything you think? When we know for a fact most of our thoughts are involuntary. We're not islands. We're shaped by how we were raised, what we've experienced, what we came into this world with, our culture, our life situation and the messages we encounter on our journey.

We don't choose our thoughts. We don't control the shape they take. Possibly, we can encourage some more than others, allow them more or less room. But we can't control what pops into our minds. We can only choose whether or not to believe it.

SEVEN

Mum, I'm going to become a forest monk

With the zeal of the western convert, I threw myself into reading books about Buddhism. One of them was called *Seeing the Way*. It described a monastery in northeast Thailand, where forest monks from all over the world lived together. It planted a seed within me: should I become a forest monk in Thailand? Every page in every book I read watered that seed. Drop by drop, the tiny seed grew and suddenly, one day, when I was sitting at the kitchen table with my mum, a small shoot poked its head out of the soil:

'Mum, I'm going to become a forest monk.'

'Okay ... Have you ever met a forest monk?'

'No. I read about them in a book.'

'Have you ever been to a forest monastery?'

'No.'

'Björn, are you sure about this?'

'Yes.'

There it was again, the feeling of making a completely independent decision. The quiet conviction of intuition. It surprised both me and my mum. Just like the first time, in Spain, it took me about five seconds to make my mind up.

My parents were, as ever, supportive. They'd slowly made their peace with my eccentric side and the fact that I wasn't interested in a conventional career. They were okay with it. They never questioned it, or any of my other decisions. Knowing I can count on my parents' unwavering support, despite my unusual life choices, has meant the world to me.

It should be noted at this point that my dad entered fatherhood as the most conservative dad in Hovås and was later promoted to most conservative dad in arch-conservative Saltsjöbaden. So for his son to drop out of a promising career in business to instead sit cross-legged in a monastery in Thailand was, all things considered, not ideal. But he took it well. He wasn't thrilled when I pierced my ear while backpacking in New Zealand, and of course my loose-fitting Nepal farmers' shirts of coarse cotton were in his eyes an odd choice of clothing. And probably in most people's. But even so, Dad was fully behind me when it mattered, always supportive of my unusual life journey.

One day, I came home and told my parents I'd decided to take the next step. From now on, I was going to live the way zealous Buddhist converts everywhere do: I was going to follow the five precepts until I became a monk.

'Okay, and what are they?' my dad asked, somewhat sceptically.

I replied that I was going to refrain from taking life or harming life. My own or that of others. I was not going to steal or engage in inappropriate sexual acts. I was not going to lie and I was going to abstain from alcohol.

When I got to the last precept, the one about not drinking, my dad said:

'That's taking it a bit far, though, don't you think?'

The other precepts sounded all right to him, but living without alcohol, that was a bit too extreme. That was where my dad drew the line.

The Buddha stresses that our relationship with our parents is special. There's value in being grateful to the people who raised you. Regardless of how well they did, they probably tried their best. That's the assumption. And when you have children of your own, there's often a moment of insight: my god, being a parent is so hard and so much work. During my last months at home, the gratitude I felt towards my parents grew and intensified.

When Mum and Dad asked me if there was anything I wanted to do before setting off for the monastery, I told them I wanted to go to the Alps, as we used to do when I was little.

Said and done. Everyone came along: Mum, Dad, and my three brothers, all grown up.

You might say the members of my family had developed fairly different lifestyles by this point, not least in terms of our circadian rhythms. I, especially, had a lot of new, peculiar habits. Around half past four in the morning, I'd sit down to meditate in the living room of the small mountain cabin we'd rented, in the faint, greenish glow of the fridge light. After a while, my three brothers would come home and almost trip over me. They'd been out clubbing until closing. I think it's a rather sweet illustration of how my life had veered off down a divergent path.

I decided to give away everything I owned before becoming a monk. I'd never taken personal ownership all that seriously, never formed any strong emotional bonds with my physical possessions, but even so I was surprised by the untamed joy that welled up inside me when I finally let go of them. It felt as if I had eight espressos coursing through my veins. Then I paid off my student loans: you're not allowed to be in debt if you want to become a forest monk.

Then I was ready, without really knowing what for. But I left Sweden without reservations. The fact that it was winter made it easier.

EIGHT

Natthiko – 'One who grows in wisdom'

On 28 January 1992, I climbed out of the tuk-tuk, pulled on my small backpack and stepped through the monastery gates for the very first time. The sign next to it read *Wat Pah Nanachat* – the International Forest Monastery. I walked under the soaring vaults of the jungle canopy and soon reached the meditation hall. It smelled of tiger balm and Chinese incense. About two dozen monks from all over the world were sitting in silence on a low dais, eating from their alms bowls.

I went to find the kitchen and ate there with the old village women. Their grandchildren played around us. Another ten or so western guests were also present. When the monks had finished eating, I approached the abbot on my knees and bowed, as I'd been told I was supposed to. His name was Ajahn Passano, and he was the son of a lumberjack from Canada's western wilderness. He smiled warmly and broadly when I told him why I was there:

'I've left everything behind and want to become a forest monk.'

He said that was nice.

'You can move into the dormitory with the other male guests. If you're still here three days from now, you'll be asked to shave your head.'

At that moment, his welcome seemed rather curt. Much later, I understood why. The abbot had seen so many people change their minds when reality didn't live up to their expectations. My conviction hadn't faded in the slightest after the first three days, though, so shaving my hair off at that point felt easy. The practice is meant to show that you're prepared to forego something to be there, that you're serious. The shaving also serves as a natural end point for guest visits. It makes it clear the monastery is first and foremost the home of monks and nuns, not a free hostel for backpackers. I underwent the ritual together with a man from New Zealand who arrived at the same time as me and who would come to be a close friend. We took photographs and had a good laugh at the funny haircuts we created as we went from relatively long-haired to completely bald.

A few weeks later, a small ceremony was held to raise me to something called a postulant, a kind of pretend monk dressed in white robes. As a postulant, you're still allowed to do things like handle money and drive a car, but you're increasingly introduced to real monastic life.

Three months after that, I became a novice. That was when I was given my monastic name.

I held our abbot and teacher, Ajahn Passano, in the greatest respect. I felt an immediate and unreserved trust for him and not once did he give me cause to question that trust. As usual during a naming ceremony, Ajahn Passano turned to the book you'll find in all Thai monasteries, which contains all the possible names you can be given, depending on what day of the week you were born on. There are hundreds of names to choose from and it's the teacher's job to select one he deems suitable. Ajahn Psasano suggested the name *Natthiko*, which means 'one who grows in wisdom', and asked me if that felt right for me. I liked it a lot and still do today.

Monks and nuns are given monastic names as a reminder of their new lifestyle. Their life as 'homeless'. It's not said whether the meaning of your monastic name is meant to strengthen some aspect of your personality or to encourage you to grow in an area where you're deficient. It probably varies. To give you one example: in our monastery we had a monk who came from a tough background – to put it mildly – and who used very coarse language, peppered with curses. That was a poor fit with monastery life, of course, so when he was given a monastic name that meant *The Well-Spoken*, it was obvious his teacher felt he needed extra encouragement in that particular area.

As a novice monk, you look like a full monk, dressed in ochre robes in our case, but you follow an easier set of rules. Not until we'd spent about a year as novices were we, if everyone agreed it was a good idea, allowed to become 'real' monks. That meant choosing to be bound by much stricter rules. Traditions vary, depending on which branch of Buddhism you belong to, but in Theravada, ordained monks follow 227 rules and nuns 311.

Ideally, you should learn to recite the rules by heart. Being able to do that comes with a certain amount of status. Of the native monks, maybe ten per cent attempted it, and about a third of us westerners. It requires an inordinate amount of practice. The rules are written in the liturgical language Pali and you have to learn to recite them extremely quickly. Once a fortnight, one of us would recite the rules aloud to the whole group. A really quick recitation took about fifty minutes and if you were slower, you made yourself unpopular, since listening was tedious. I did learn, in the end, but it was one of the hardest things I've ever done. I'm not exaggerating when I say it took a thousand hours to get those rules down pat.

There are four rules that stand out. Break one of them and you're no longer a monk or nun. Everyone knows it, no one even has to point out to you that you've done something wrong. The first is theft, the second intercourse, the third causing another human's death and the fourth is to lie deliberately about reaching levels of extraordinary spiritual development when you haven't.

Some of the most common questions I've been asked since coming home have been about celibacy and abstaining from masturbation for such a long time. Many men want to know, for example, if nocturnal emissions count. Involuntary bodily reactions are never held against you. The Thai are, generally speaking, very forgiving when it comes to physical shortcomings. Minor breaches in that area are usually cause for embarrassment and giggling rather than actual shame. It's considered very human. Intercourse, on the other hand, was unthinkable. Personally, I don't believe celibacy is important to spiritual growth, but it was simply part of the deal. There were many rules I might have quibbled with, but when you choose to join that kind of community you have to go all in.

Since the time of the Buddha, monastic tradition has been to gather once a fortnight, when the moon is full and when it's new. It's a day of observance, before which everyone shaves their heads and the meditation hall is decorated with lotus flowers and incense. This is when the full recitation of the monastic rules takes place. But before that, you pair up, kneel down face to face and confess to any minor rules you may have broken or bent. If you had killed a mosquito, for instance, knowing full well you shouldn't have, you could admit to it then, but if you had broken a major rule, you had to bring it up later, in front of the entire group.

The Buddha tells us there are two ways to keep a pure heart: either you do nothing wrong, or you admit to your transgressions. A bit like Catholic confession. If, for example, you had pleasured yourself sexually, in a way prohibited in our tradition, you had to tell the group. It was often the same people confessing every time. The same monks would sheepishly crawl out into the moonlight on their knees and mumble something along the lines of: '*I might possibly have maybe done something a bit like, ehm* ...'

That particular part was obviously just a little bit comical but seeing and identifying with the failures of the others helped bring us closer together. We weren't alone in our shortcomings. And as soon as it was said out loud, the pressure inside eased slightly.

The western monks in the monastery also held regular so-called 'heart meetings', on our own initiative, during which we shared our thoughts and experiences with each other. We felt it complemented the Buddhist life-style. During these meetings, we used a vajra (a small Tibetan Buddhist symbol); the person holding it would tell the rest what they'd found difficult and challenging or encouraging since the last meeting. No one would inter-rupt, comment on or analyse what anyone else said; each person simply spoke from the heart while the others listened with theirs open. The Thai monks chuckled at these gatherings; they found them very western and organised. To them, it felt more natural to talk to each other about such things in less structured settings. But they still participated, and these meetings were often beautiful moments that strengthened our sense of community.

The Thai forest tradition was established as a response to monks and nuns abandoning the monastic code set out by the Buddha. Consequently, a forest monk's or nun's life is characterised by a focus on meditation, simplicity and ethics. We lived in small huts on tall poles, spread out in the jungle. We slept on simple bast mats. We ate only once a day. We never handled money. We were celibate. There was a lot to get used to.

And then there was the meditation. Considering that I was quite possibly the worst meditator ever, I wasn't exactly a perfect candidate for monastic life. I was unable to sit cross-legged and meditate for more than thirty to forty-five minutes before dozing off. And as we know, resisting my inner monkey circus had always been a challenge for me. It took me many, many years to master it, despite an intensive training programme that mandated hours of meditation every day. This is what my thoughts could be like when we gathered at half past three in the morning for our communal meditation:

Okay, one breath at a time. I can let everything else go now. In. Out. In. Out. I wonder how long it takes to reach enlightenment? It only took the Buddha six years. But I bet he had a bunch of lives with perfect karma behind him. I don't really know what my karma looks like. But perfect definitely isn't the word for it. I wonder how many beers I've had, just in this lifetime? Five thousand? Ten thousand? If you were to stack the crates, how tall would the stack be? Let's see ... No! No! Focus, mister, focus! Let's go! Mindfulness is only ever as far away as your next breath. Patience, patience. Rome wasn't built in a day. Sit like the Zen monks in Japan. Zen, right ... Those guys are classy. They have flair. Nicer statues. Straighter backs. Calligraphy. Haikus. Rock gardens. I think they even have a tipple from time to time ... Oh come on! Seriously! Stop speculating! Be present! Inhale. Exhale. Ah. Here comes stillness. Ow! What happened?! Did someone just hit me in the head? Surely that's impossible? I'd open my eyes. The tiled floor would be less than two inches away. *Oops. I must have fallen asleep, tipped forward and hit my head on the floor. Embarrassing. I wonder if anyone noticed?*

Despite the many challenges, I never doubted my decision to become a monk. That voice inside my head, the one that had always whispered that 'life is somewhere else', had finally fallen silent.

In the western world, not least in business, I'd been told the intellect trumps virtually everything. But here, I was given convincing proof of what I'd long suspected – that we humans have so many other resources at our disposal, too. There exists an intelligence that isn't confined to our heads, and we would do well to turn to it more.

That wise voice inside me, the one that had brought me all the way here, it's worth listening to.

For the first time in my life, I felt the world agreed with me about what was important: being present in everything you do. Telling the truth. Helping each other. And trusting silence more than chattering thoughts. It was like coming home.

NINE

The intelligence of the moment

Our Thai forest tradition was founded by a remarkably jolly monk by the name of Ajahn Chah. His spiritual awakening, in combination with his humorous and
loving personality, made him an inspiration to many and
attracted a lot of followers. In the 1960s and 1970s, he
became increasingly popular in Buddhist circles, not least
among old hippies who had previously kept to India, and
a lot of people found their way to his monastery in north-
east Thailand. Because the Thai dialect in this area is so
challenging, and because many of Ajahn Chah's followers
were westerners, it soon became clear there was a need
for an English-language monastery. Not long thereafter, a
nearby plot of land was donated for this purpose and that
is how our, at the time completely unique, international
forest monastery came to be.

Ajahn Chah was something of a spiritual hero to many
of us. He had an extraordinarily wide face and an equally

wide smile that rarely left it. What else could we call him but The Bullfrog?

On one occasion, Ajahn Chah was sitting on a small bamboo cot in the jungle outside the monastery, surrounded by monks and nuns. He picked up a machete, held it up in front of him and said something like:

> You know what? Our intellect is in some ways similar to this knife. Imagine if I used this knife all the time, to cut plastic, concrete, glass, metal, wood and stone, then it would soon become dull, unable to do its job effectively. If I let the knife rest in its sheath, on the other hand, except for when it was time to cut wood or bamboo, then it would do its job sharply, quickly and effectively for a long, long time.

I like that simile. In order to keep my intellect as functional as possible, as sharp and effective as I want it to be, it needs to rest from time to time.

It's so easy to forget that we humans have more than one way of reaching knowledge. It's so easy to forget that reason isn't the only tool in our toolbox. I'm not saying it's not a beautiful and important aspect of our nature. It has given us a lot of good and beautiful things: technology, science, healthcare, democracy, equality – countless valuable ideas and systems. But there's more to us than just reason. We also have another way of reaching knowledge and making decisions. We have moments of inspiration.

Buddhists call this wisdom. And they see a clear link between meditation and wisdom.

Sometimes, when I listen inwardly, things suddenly seem clear. That was exactly what happened to me that Sunday afternoon on my sofa in Spain. Some call it following your heart, some call it intuition. For my part, I prefer to call it *the intelligence of the moment*. It doesn't matter what we call it or how we find it. But realising that we humans have that ability does matter. Precisely because we are human, we have the ability to listen to the voice of our wisdom. It's in there. Too many people don't hear it. Not least in these times when it's so easy to look for external answers. Giving our intellect a rest and quietly turning inward to listen has probably never been harder, never required more of us than it does now.

It's easy to get caught up in thinking happiness comes from external factors. That's exactly what happened to me as a young adult and to this day I'm not immune to it. The gravitational pull of it is very strong. Appearing successful to others, by, for example, having an impressive career, can boost your ego for a while. But if you stop and think about it, you'll soon realise it's a bit like trying to live off nothing but sweets. Sweets are colourful, fun and delicious at the time. But they don't provide lasting sustenance.

We all have access to the intelligence of the moment. There's a finely honed, quiet compass inside each of us.

All we have to do is pay attention, because our wisdom isn't as loud as our ego. Our ego often drowns out everything else with its noisy demands. That's why it can make sense to turn the frequency to a different wavelength from time to time. To find moments of stillness in our everyday lives, in whatever way makes sense to us. It's an amazing ability, worth nurturing. If we don't, our attention will invariably be drawn to whatever shouts the loudest at any given moment. That leads to drama. That leads to conflict. That leads to anxiety and unhappiness. A constant struggle against reality.

Listening to your inner voice isn't anti-rational; it *includes* the rational. It doesn't mean completely novel thoughts and notions suddenly strike like bolts from the blue. Indeed, they may very likely be the result of extensive mulling over long periods of time. That was what it was like for me when I decided to quit that fancy job. Those thoughts had been there for a while, running in the background. But as we all know, it's very difficult to question something in which you've invested so much time and ambition. It's difficult to give up something that looks right and proper on paper, be it a job, a relationship, a lifestyle. But when I let go of my thoughts a little, allow them to flow more freely, I'm able to make room for a truer conviction. It's usually only then, when I let the wiser voice inside me make itself heard, that I can come to a final decision. I haven't *reasoned* my way to this or that. There wasn't a thought that led to a thought that led to a conclusion. It's just suddenly clear to me, in a moment of stillness when I have access to a larger part of myself.

Or, as a wise man called Albert Einstein once said: 'The rational mind is a servant. The intuitive mind is a sacred gift. We have created a society that honours the servant and has forgotten the gift.'

TEN

The eccentric commune

When I first made the decision to become a monk, I had some firm ideas of what a Buddhist monastery should look like and what life in one would be like. I had to revise quite a few of them.

First, each monastery looks different. There's everything from run-down, busy monasteries in the middle of residential areas to monasteries of significant beauty in the bosom of nature, consisting of scattered little bamboo huts. I also quickly realised that whichever monastery I ended up at, I'd have to abandon one of my reasons for wanting to become a monk in the first place – that is, the idea that I would finally be left alone. Truly alone.

After just a few weeks it had become clear to me that I'd joined a 24/7 commune, consisting of some of the most eccentric people I'd ever met. We weren't allowed to choose our roommates. We swapped rooms or huts once a month, partly to discourage us from clinging too tightly to something we thought of as 'our own' and partly because there was a lot of coming and going. People you liked might suddenly leave the monastery while others you found less pleasant stayed forever, or at least it seemed as if they did. Social training was apparently going to be a central part of my monastic life. That was definitely not what I'd expected.

At first, it was a huge challenge for me. I had a tendency to compare myself too much to the other monks. I tormented myself with thoughts like: 'You're not as intelligent as Sujato. You're not as empathetic as Nyanarato. Not as patient as Tejapañño. Not as mindful as Chandako.' At the same time, every single one of them irked me in one way or another. People can really get on your nerves, can't they! They annoyed me; I was upset when they didn't behave like I felt they should. But after a while, I recognised the pain in all that resistance I was creating inside myself. Slowly but surely, something inside me became a little more generous. I learned not to have so many opinions about others, to let them be the way they were. Our abbot encouraged us to think of it this way:

All of us are like pebbles washed up on a beach. When we get there, we're rough and jagged. Then the waves of life roll in. And if we can find it in us to stay there and let the other pebbles on the beach jostle us and rub against us and wear us down, our sharp edges will slowly but surely fade. We'll become rounded and smooth, we'll reflect the light and begin to shine.

It's only human to find other people annoying. It happens to all of us. But it's a huge energy suck and can turn into an unnecessary drain on your resources. I'm happy to tell you there's a solution to the problem. If you want someone to be easy to deal with, to behave in a way you find tolerable, there's really only one way: learn to like them exactly as they are.

Because when has anyone, in the entire history of the universe, ever become more like someone else thought they ought to be, simply because that person walked around judging them? And yet, we keep doing it. It's astonishing to the point of almost being adorable. We think we're so omnipotent. '*I know what everyone should be like and I'm going to make myself suffer psychologically if they refuse to comply.*' We really think a lot of ourselves!

We human beings have bullshit detectors. We can sense when someone has reservations. It undermines our confidence and puts our backs up. It makes us less caring, less emotionally accessible. And it works the other way, too. We can sense when someone seems to be thinking: Hi! *You're welcome just the way you are, it's so lovely that you're you. You don't have to be any other way, I accept all your idiosyncrasies, your quirks and eccentric sides, your odd behaviours; you're completely welcome in my world just the way you are. There's room here for you.*

Imagine being greeted like that instead. That would automatically make you easier to be around.

We can get so far by just letting each other be who we are, by accepting each other. That way, we give each other a chance to move forward with all of our strengths, all of our talents, a chance to become more beautiful versions of ourselves. When we feel assured others accept us for who we are, it's easier for us to be sensitive to others. It makes us able to interact with our surroundings in a more empathetic way.

These things come to the fore when you live in a commune – not least a commune dedicated full-time to spiritual and personal growth. The people I found most objectionable at first were often the ones I eventually came to like the most, once I had worked through my reservations. There was a monk from Oklahoma who hated me intensely for four years. Daily, openly, relentlessly. It's almost ironic in hindsight, since I was a person who struggled with caring too much about what other people thought of me. It's something I've had to work very hard on. I needed someone to hate me, just so that I could see for myself how pointless it is to always want to be liked by everyone.

In other words, commune life had many ancillary benefits. One of my immediate favourite aspects of monastic life was the inclusivity. I like it when everyone's allowed to join. You don't have to be smart to become a monk or nun. You don't have to do well in school or even be particularly mentally mature to join a monastery.

All that's required is that you demonstrate your good intentions and do the best you can.

The culture in a monastery of the forest tradition is based on consensus. The monks or nuns who live there have to express to one another that '*I'm prepared to work with you. You don't have to be perfect, you don't have to be intellectually shrewd, I don't even have to like you. But I'm prepared to work with you.*' It was a fundamental part of monastic life, to do everything together. And all our chores were underpinned by a principle that appealed to me: whatever you do, be present. No activity is more valuable than any other. It's not better or fancier to give a lecture to nurses from the local hospital than to sweep a path, than to do dishes, than to tidy up.

So even if things didn't turn out the way I thought they would before I went, they turned out exactly the way they were meant to. We learned to live together by doing just that. And as the waves rolled in, we found it in ourselves to stay on that beach and rub our sharp edges together until we became smoother.

ELEVEN

The rhythm of a forest monastery

The first time my parents came to visit the monastery, I'd been a monk for a year. I had all the zeal of the newly converted and was extremely gung-ho about my new life. I felt I'd found it and I now had access to the answers to *everything*. In my world, there were no important questions the Buddha couldn't answer. But what would Mum and Dad think?

Dad seemed to spend most of his visit looking for out-of-the-way places for a sneaky cigarette, since smoking was forbidden in the monastery grounds. On the third day of their stay, I was unable to contain myself any longer.

'So, Dad, what do you think, about this place and the way we live here?'

Dad looked at me, took a drag on his cigarette and said:

'I guess it's a bit like the Scouts. But with more morals.'

Mum's approach to the monastery was more hands-on. The morning after they arrived, she emerged from their tiny guest hut carrying a giant slab of vacuum-packed salmon. She marched over to the primitive monastery kitchen where food was cooked over an open flame and announced:

'I'm making salmon hors d'oeuvres for all the monks and nuns!'

She'd brought the mustard sauce all the way from Sweden, of course.

Before we sat down to eat that day, I noticed Mum was very eager to talk to our teacher, head monk Ajahn Passano. But she also knew mealtimes are fairly cere-monial in a Thai monastery and not the time to inter-rupt. The monks (and any nuns who may be present) sit down, sing a blessing and eat in silence. The guests typic-ally take their meals in the kitchen where the atmosphere is completely different, almost festive.

Grandmothers from the surrounding villages use the monastery as a social club. They arrive in the morning, bringing their grandchildren along and spend most of the day in the kitchen, gossiping and lending the cooks a hand. They were kind enough to make some kind of vegetable stir fry as often as they could, since they knew most of us westerners preferred vegetarian food, which is otherwise unusual in rural Thailand. Mum loved hanging out in the monastery kitchen. She likes being around people and is very fond of children. She felt right at home even though she didn't understand a word of what anyone said.

As soon as the monks had finished their meal and our Canadian teacher Ajahn Passano had put down his spoon, Mum sidled up to him and said:

'Hi, my name is Kylle, I'm Natthiko's mother. How long was it before you went home to visit your parents after you became a monk?'

Ajahn Passano replied: 'My dear Kylle, what an unfortunate first question. Because you know what; I'd only been a monk for three years when they asked me if I would agree to be the abbot here. It's not a popular job. You're always busy and people project a lot of things onto you. People who come here to be monks and nuns have given up a lot to do so and they have many expectations and fears. So this is a sensitive job. It's almost like being a public figure, there's a lot of responsibility. And remember, most of us came here to live a quieter, more secluded life. But I felt the only decent thing to do, since no one else was willing, was to accept that responsibility and say yes. It made me so busy, I didn't have a single week off for twelve years. In other words, it was sixteen years before I went back home to visit my family.'

That was definitely not what my mum wanted to hear. I couldn't make out her response, but her face said something along the lines of: *'There's no way Björn's staying away from his family that long.'*

My use of the English word *abbot* is a bit infelicitous because of its strong Christian connotations. It tends to evoke an image of a squat, medieval monk making cheese. But I haven't been able to think of a better translation for the head of a Buddhist monastery, so I guess I'm stuck with it. Anyway, it does the job of explaining who the head honcho is. In addition to the abbot, there are senior monks. That's anyone who has been part of the order for at least ten years. Being a senior monk grants you use of the title *Ajahn*, which is really Thai for 'teacher'.

Our monastery was unique because it housed monks from so many different countries. Sometimes, our cultural difference became particularly noticeable. Hierarchical structure, for example, was an area where the western and Southeast Asian monks had very different cultural expectations. Thailand is by tradition patriarchal and hierarchical. The Thai monks, and those from other countries in the region, approached monastic life according to a *family* paradigm. The abbot was their 'father'. Seen from that perspective, a clear hierarchy was considered normal and the leader, the father figure, was inherently trusted. Us western monks instead approached monastic life according to a *work* paradigm, which cast the abbot in a role closer to 'the boss'. This entailed a lower degree of inherent trust and a different attitude to duties and the division of labour.

Life in Thailand is also to a larger extent ruled by emotion. It's perfectly fine there to simply say 'I don't feel good about this' when chores or decisions are being discussed. For those of us who had grown up in the organisational culture of the West, it was challenging to understand how that kind of argument could be given so much weight.

Thai monastic life is built around routine and therefore relatively predictable. It made life naturally restful. There were far fewer impressions to process in a day there than in the western world, so your mind was less exhausted at the end of it. It soon became very clear to me that my brain was much less busy now.

Our alarms would go off at 3 a.m. Half an hour later we all gathered in one of our two meditation halls. I never quite got used to the nocturnal procession and in the dark every last tree root meandering across the path looking like a snake. Actually, sometimes it was a snake, so there was no point in trying to convince myself it was all in my head. Since there was a certain amount of prestige in having as few possessions as possible, some monks insisted on walking the path barefoot and without torches. Twice, I stepped on a snake and I was badly shaken both times. These aren't grass snakes we're talking about, after all. Someone tried to reassure me afterwards by telling me the reason the snake was so slow and didn't manage to bite me was that it was one of the most venomous snakes in the jungle and they have less reason to be fast.

'Great, thanks, that makes me feel much better.'

The meditation hall at the edge of the jungle was built without walls so that the wind could blow through it. The roof was held up by columns and there was a golden Buddha statue at one end of the tiled floor. Several remarkably beautiful ceiling fans did their best to keep the mosquitoes away. Upon entering the hall, we'd kneel and bow. It's similar to a Muslim bow: we'd put our feet and knees on the floor and then slowly touch the palms of our hands and our foreheads to the floor as well.

The meditation hall wasn't the only place that required ritual bowing. In a forest temple, convention dictates that any time you sit down in a room, any room, where there's a Buddha statue, you first bow three times to that statue. And when you get back up, you bow again, three times. Since sitting down and getting up occurs quite a few times a day, and since practically all rooms in a forest monastery contain at least one Buddha statue, there was a lot of bowing. At first, I found the practice peculiar, strange. But in time I came to understand its significance.

The Buddha was very wise and clear about the nature of ritual. Rituals and ceremonies have no intrinsic meaning.

We *endow* them with meaning. As a monk or nun, you're supposed to endow all your actions with meaning that's significant to *you*.

In time, the bowing provided me with a growing sense of confidence, an ever more all-encompassing conviction, that there existed a sager source of wisdom in this world than my own noisy little ego.

After the initial bowing, we'd sing. Unlike Jesus, Buddha had forty-five years to share the discoveries he made from the age of thirty-five onwards. And tens of thousands of contemporary nuns and monks made a hobby of memorising what the Buddha said when he answered his congregation's questions. As a consequence, the Buddha's words and teachings have been preserved in a rich collection of songs and texts. The singing was followed by an extended period of meditation, the first of the day.

Monks are not allowed to leave the monastery before the sun rises, but, once dawn broke, it was time for us to go out in search of alms – my favourite part of the day. We went in groups of five or six, scattering in different directions. Always walking barefoot, single file, in silence through the village. We all had bowls hung on cords around our necks. People who were willing and able to give us some homecooked food would generally be waiting by the side of the road, or they would call from their houses that they would be out in a minute and politely ask us to wait.

At the end of our rounds, we returned to the monastery with the gifts we had received. It might be fruit, rice, eggs, plastic bags containing cooked meals, desserts wrapped in banana leaves. None of the food was anyone's personal property, everything was considered communal and deposited on enormous enamel platters that were then brought to the kitchen. There, the things that needed cooking were cooked, and everything was plated for serving. Maybe some people in a nearby village was celebrating someone's birthday or marking the death day of a beloved family member. On such days, the family would often bring food to the monastery.

There was always plenty to eat in the monastery. More than enough. Locals were welcome to visit the monastery kitchen and were always offered a meal when they came, whether or not they were in need. After all, this part of Thailand was very poor. The same went for any donations we received – anything not used was passed on. And since our monastery enjoyed a good reputation, we had a lot of supporters, including wealthy people from the big cities, who were happy to contribute. Thanks to them, our monastery was, to give just one example, able to fund the largest wing of the local hospital. So that was a wonderful redistribution of resources and mutual dependence between us and the local population.

At 8.30 a.m. we'd sit down for the only meal of the day. It took me years to get used to eating just once a day! At first, I spent large parts of my walking meditations thinking of nothing but pizza and ice cream. Monks, nuns and guests who had spent at least three days at the monastery were expected to be seated and ready in the meditation hall by the kitchen half an hour before the food was served. The idea was to eat mindfully. It was an important aspect of the contemplative mood around mealtime. We'd sit on a knee-high platform and eat, silently and attentively. The seating arrangement was based on seniority. The person who had worn their robes the longest sat closest to the Buddha and was served first.

The meal would be over by 9.30. Then the monks had 'free time' until 3 p.m. Many of us spent a large part of that time doing walking meditation. This was my favourite activity. There was also seated meditation, yoga, tai chi, studying, reading, writing, gossiping, cleaning, doing laundry and napping.

The hours between 3 p.m. and 5 p.m. were dedicated to work. This often involved strenuous physical labour. We did live in a tropical jungle after all, so there was a lot of vegetation to cut back and tend to. Sometimes, up to a hundred people might line up to pass small buckets of cement back and forth. There was always something that needed building, fixing, repairing. Or the filter in the tank we collected rainwater in might need seeing to, or someone had to go online to renew visas.

One chore that often fell to me was to look after the many guests who visited our monastery. We all had different areas of responsibility, for longer or shorter periods, and I spent half of my monastic life as a guest monk. The fact that I spoke six languages came in handy, of course, and for the most part I thought it was a pleasant task, even though you had to be prepared to be disturbed a lot. Since our monastery was uniquely international, it was a popular place to visit. Coaches full of tourists eager to see how we lived arrived almost daily. Many Thai people found western monks to be incredibly exotic Being a monk was considered very difficult even for a native. And then we came along, from the West, having given up everything to follow the Buddha. And we stuck with it! It was a source of pride for the Thai, who were very impressed by us.

At 5 p.m., it was finally time for a much-anticipated tea and coffee break. We monks had fasted since 9 a.m., drinking only water, so the sweet, hot beverages were beyond welcome by late afternoon. Personally, I suffered from a severe coffee addiction, and the lack of it no doubt had something to do with my persistent inability to stay awake. Teatime was often fun and enjoyable. Sometimes, our teacher would invite us to ask questions, sometimes he'd just philosophise out loud.

Around 6.30 to 7 p.m. we'd get up and rinse out our cups. It was an ideal time for me to meditate for a while since I had caffeine in my system and therefore tend not to nod off quite so easily. At half past eight, we'd all gather in the meditation hall again and go through roughly the same routine as in the morning – we'd bow, sing, meditate. A normal day was over around nine o'clock. Once or twice a week, our teacher would give an evening lecture, and those days it was often closer to ten before we headed off to bed.

I remember one night particularly vividly. After the tea break I'd gone off to meditate by myself for a while. It was almost seven and dark in my hut apart from the light of a few candles. I was sitting there by myself when I heard a voice by my shoulder. It was a monk friend of mine who'd come to tell me someone in the kitchen was asking for me. It was highly unusual for anyone to disturb someone when they were meditating, so I obviously wondered who it might be, but my friend wasn't forthcoming. We picked up our torches and lit our way back to the kitchen building.

From afar I could only make out the vague shape of two people in the gloom, and, when we got closer, a bright spotlight was suddenly turned on. Blinded, I began to blink frantically, and I could sense someone was sticking something fluffy in my face, which I identified as a microphone with a windscreen. When I looked up, I could finally see the person holding it. It was a face I knew and, in all my Buddhist wisdom, the only words that came to me were:

'I've seen you on TV!' It was Swedish journalist Stina Dabrowski.

Stina and her crew had come to Thailand to interview King Bhumibol, but he had cancelled their meeting at the last minute. Someone at the Swedish consulate had then told her there was this Swede, a former economist, who was playing at being a forest monk in the jungle near the Laotian border. Stina and her cameraman were hoping a visit to our monastery might still make their long trip worthwhile. They stayed with us for twenty-four hours and Stina tagged along when we did our alms round the next morning. She gave each of us a handful of bananas to put in our bowls.

After breakfast, Stina and her cameraman had prepared a lovely spot in the jungle, with a rug laid out for us to sit on while she interviewed me. Stina's reaction to our monastery was mixed: on the one hand, it seemed like a thoroughly decent place where people were kind, calm and gentle and listened to and helped one another. Put more succinctly, people were mindful. And that's easy to like. On the other hand, the monastery residents had chosen to turn their backs on everything 'regular people' seem to prioritise in life, from after-work drinks and dinner parties with friends to having children or romantic relationships. It's a choice many people find provocative.

Perhaps the provoked part of Stina was in charge when she asked the question: 'But really, Björn, what would become of the world if everyone decided they wanted to be a monk or a nun?'

I calmly replied:

'Stina, I think it would turn out at least as well as if everyone decided they wanted to be a broadcast journalist.'

TWELVE

Kitschy wisdom

It can be hard to imagine how utterly devoid of stimulation a Thai forest monastery is. There was obviously no access to the kind of entertainment or popular culture with which we westerners have become so used to distracting ourselves. The best-read books in the monastery library were the ones my brother was nice enough to send me every year for Christmas and my birthday, *Calvin and Hobbes* comic books. Surprisingly, many of us appreciated these literary gems. You should have seen how tattered and frayed they were! One monk who was particularly fond of *Calvin and Hobbes* was Kondañño. A funny thing about him was that he was *completely* uninterested in anything to do with meditation and Buddhism. He only really liked the practical aspects of monastic life. Like building things. Or reading comic books.

One day, I was sitting in the meditation hall, waiting for my daily meal. As I've mentioned before, it's easy to get overly focused on food when you fast for twenty-three and a half hours a day. I was verging on the obsessed. So I sat there, poised and ready, having noted that my favourite dish was present in the buffet that day – a kind of thick, sticky rice, boiled in coconut cream and served with fresh, ripe mango. The thought of that dessert made it especially difficult for me to wait patiently and with gratitude for the food we'd been given that day. I was too busy trying to estimate if there would be enough to go round until it was my turn. Since I was relatively new to the monastery at that point, a lot of people were served before me. I looked around a bit anxiously, trying to find something other than food to think about. A very colourful plastic cylinder on my right caught my eye.

At the Stockholm School of Economics we were taught that for a market economy to thrive there must be a free flow of information, so that all actors have access to the same data. The economy of the monastery was in many ways very imperfect. Our monastic life was funded entirely by donations, alms and generosity. We never asked for anything; the only exception to this rule was that we were allowed to respond if someone announced that they wanted to help us and wanted to know how best to do so. For the most part, though, people simply brought us what they thought we needed. Among other things, this led to a great surplus of certain products, such as toilet paper. We had enormous quantities of toilet paper!

Our creativity was tested to its limits as we constantly searched for new ways of making constructive use of all that tissue.

On a visit to Japan, one of the monastery's wealthy Bangkok supporters had discovered a kind of hollow plastic cylinder you could place over a roll of toilet paper. Then you loosened the cardboard tube at the centre of the roll and that way you could pull out appropriate lengths of tissue through the hole in the middle, turning an unsightly toilet paper roll into a handy napkin dispenser fit for a dining table.

It's well known that the people of Asia, and perhaps the Japanese especially, have a certain penchant for the kitsch. The aforementioned plastic cylinder was an excellent example of this. And there I sat, all but mesmerised by a bright yellow and hot pink Hello Kitty dispenser.

Understimulated as I was, I picked it up to have a closer look, to see if there was anything written on it. It was just like when I was little, before mobile phones, when people would read the back of the milk carton over breakfast. And I wasn't disappointed. At the very bottom, around the base of the cylinder, I was delighted to discover a few words in English. The text read: *Knowledge is proud of all it knows. Wisdom is humble before all it doesn't know.*

Who would have thought it! Timeless wisdom, piggybacking on a garish plastic cylinder. It reminded me that there's value in not getting stuck in a state of certainty.

If you always cling to what you think you already know, you make yourself inaccessible, and you miss out on so much. If we want access to a higher wisdom, we have to let go of some of our convictions and become more comfortable with not knowing. Thinking that we know is often a big problem. Knowing you don't know is hardly ever a big problem.

If we always cling to what we think we already know, how will we ever discover anything new? How can we learn? How can we stretch, improvise, play? How can we find a way to make one plus one come out as three?

If you want to know what a person feels like who has never listened to the voice of their inner wisdom, who's eternally hypnotised by their own thoughts, who's unyieldingly certain, let me give you a pedagogical example taken from a work from that canon of western wisdom, *Winnie-the-Pooh*:

In this particular scene, Pooh and Piglet are out walking together. I'm sure you can picture it: Pooh in his little red T-shirt and Piglet in his pink bathing suit. After stopping by Rabbit's home, Pooh says: 'Rabbit's clever.' 'Yes,' Piglet replies, 'Rabbit is clever.' 'And he has Brain,' continues Pooh. 'Yes,' says Piglet, 'Rabbit has Brain.' There's a long silence, then Pooh says: 'I suppose that that's why he never understands anything.'

We can all relate to this. People who are caught up in the fog of their own thinking, they're not present.

They're limited. Rabbit may be clever and have brains. But if asked whether I would rather live my life as Rabbit or Winnie-the-Pooh, the answer is obvious, at least for me. And I think it behoves all of us to locate our inner Winnie-the-Pooh. To go into the world as Pooh would – wide-eyed, alert, aware.

Opening up to a Rabbit, a person who clings to what they think they already know, rarely gives me any pleasure. I usually end up feeling as if they're not listening, as if they're too busy thinking about what they're going to say the second I finally stop talking. They also have a ten-dency continually to assess and review what I say. My opinions and perspectives are approved to the extent that they confirm and agree with their worldview. There's no magic being made there. Put another way, people like that aren't fun to be around.

And the opposite – we all know how good it can be to open up to a person who gives us a bit of attention, who listens openly and with curiosity, right? A person who might even be capable of putting themselves in our shoes for a moment and walk by our side for a bit. That kind of listening is genuinely healing. When we meet on that level, we can learn a lot about ourselves: *Wow, look at me, sharing and explaining, saying things I didn't realise I thought or felt or believed. How exciting!* Listening without prejudice or judgement can help us understand ourselves. And that's no small thing. There's something there.

As I'm sure you've noticed by now, I'm a big fan of stories. I don't know where this particular one is from, but I want to tell it anyway. It's about a man who's climbing a mountain. He has already made it halfway to the top and he can see how steep the mountainside is. The path is narrow and slick with rain. In the middle of it, there's a round stone that's extra slippery. The man doesn't see it, so he steps on it, slips and falls over the edge. Desperately, he throws out his arms for something to hold onto. Miraculously, he manages to grab hold of a small tree growing horizontally out of the rock. And there he hangs.

This is a man with no previous spiritual interest, who has never expressed any religious beliefs. Time passes. Slowly, the strength begins to seep from his arms. They start to tremble. There's fifteen hundred feet of air below him. A fifteen-hundred-foot drop. Eventually, he starts to panic because he realises he won't be able to hold on for much longer. Then he turns to the sky and says tentatively:

'Hello? God? Can you hear me? I could really use some help, if you do exist?'

After a moment, a deep, commanding voice is heard from the sky:

'This is God. I can help you. But you have to do exactly as I say.'

The man:

'Anything, God, anything at all!'

80

God:

'Let go.'

The man thinks about that for a few seconds and then says:

'Err ... Is there anyone else up there I could talk to?'

This story speaks to me. Because that's *exactly* how I feel whenever I find myself stuck in unyielding conviction. I *don't want* to let go of this thought, because it's *right*.

We all get entangled in this 'logic' sometimes. Especially when we're feeling low. We cling to certain fixed beliefs. Maybe we recall reading something in a book about how it's easy to underestimate how much our thoughts can harm us, how much unnecessary mental suffering we create for ourselves by believing in things that do us harm. But at the next moment, we think: *'Sure, that sounds smart. But this thought, I'm never letting go of this one. This one's true, this one's correct.'*

Yes, from your limited perspective at that moment, it's unquestionable. But what *effect* does it have on you?

Practising letting go is one of the most important things I've learned. The wisdom of that is profound. We never stop benefiting from getting better at it. The only way to get rid of thoughts that are harming us, that are making us feel small, useless, lonely, afraid, sad, angry – is to let them go. Even if they're 'right'. That's obviously easier said than done. But it's worth noting that, at the end of the day, it's the thoughts we have real trouble letting go of that tend to harm us the most.

THIRTEEN

The Magic Mantra

Once a week, we meditated throughout the night. From time to time, there was singing and bowing, too, but the majority of the night was spent in silent meditation. It was a bit like the Buddhist equivalent of a Sunday, a relatively solemn occasion. I always looked forward to these nights with a mixture of apprehension and delight. Delight, because they were so beautiful. Apprehension, because I had such a hard time staying awake.

One night stands out in my memory. It was a full moon. Clear sky. No wind. We were gathering in the beautiful meditation hall with its big, unglazed windows. An astonishing range of sounds could be heard from the jungle outside: birds, insects, the rustling of leaves as animals moved about. The familiar smell of incense and tiger balm came and went. Hundreds of candles illuminated the hall, which had been beautifully decorated with lotus flowers, and the two enormous, gleaming brass Buddhas watching over us. They were approximately ten feet tall and every week, the day before one of these nocturnal meditations, thirty monks would polish every inch of them with Brasso to make them look even more golden in the candlelight.

The hall filled up with monks and congregants. Eventually, about 150 people were meditating cross-legged on the floor. Well, I assume the other 149 were meditating. For me, the all-night meditations were a long exercise in humiliation. I found it virtually impossible not to nod off. I really did try. I suspect I looked a bit like a ship in the night, swaying back and forth in my exhaustion.

Ironic, isn't it? I'd given up so much for this. Abandoned a promising career, given away all my possessions, left my loved ones – all to be a forest monk in Thailand. And the one thing Buddhist monks and nuns are supposed to spend so much of their time doing, I was apparently incapable of.

To my relief, around midnight, things began to look up. That was when our American novice monk, a former jazz pianist, brought in several aluminium cauldrons. Together with a few of the other novices, he'd spent the past hour making strong, sweet coffee for the rest of us. Those of us who lived in the monastery were seated along one side of the beautiful, airy hall. Twenty monks from almost as many countries. We drank our coffee with reverence. Someone joked that with such outstanding coffee-making skills, this particular novice was destined for greatness.

Eventually, our teacher walked up to the front of the hall to start the evening's lecture. My first abbot, Ajahn Passano, had left Thailand to start a new monastery in the US. He had been succeeded by another remarkable monk – Ajahn Jayasaro from the UK. He sat down on the floor with his legs crossed and adjusted his ochre robe. Ajahn Jayasaro has an exceptionally open heart and a razor-sharp mind and the channel between the two is completely unobstructed.

Everyone in the room, monks and congregants, was paying rapt attention. Ajahn Jayasaro is a skilled speaker and on this particular night he unexpectedly began by saying:

'Tonight, I want to give you a magic mantra.'

We were all taken aback. The forest tradition is known for rejecting anything to do with magic and mysticism. It sees no value in such things. Ajahn Jayasaro calmly continued in his almost impeccable Thai:

'The next time you sense a conflict brewing, when you feel things are about to come to a head with someone, just repeat this mantra to yourself three times, sincerely and convincingly – in any language you want – and your worries will evaporate, like dew from the grass on a summer morning.'

He had all of us in the palm of his hand. The silence was absolute and every ear strained to hear his next words. He leaned forward slightly, paused for effect and then said:

'All right, are you with me? Here's the magic mantra:

I may be wrong.

I may be wrong.

I may be wrong.'

It's been twenty years since that night, but I still think about it. Maybe you know that feeling, when your body recognises and reacts to truth, far quicker than your brain is able to parse it. Those things stick with you. Forever.

That being said, I'll be the first to admit that this mantra is especially challenging to remember when I need it the most. But when I do remember it, it always works. It always propels me forward, in a humbler, more constructive direction. This wisdom is timeless and obviously doesn't belong to any one religion.

I may be wrong. So simple. So true. So easy to forget.

I once told the story of the magic mantra during a lecture that my wife Elisabeth attended. The next morning we quarrelled about something over breakfast. My obstinate inner four-year-old is worryingly close to the surface sometimes, so I allowed myself to get worked up over something trivial. I was sullen in that way people are sullen when they know, even as they're becoming sullen, that they don't have a leg to stand on, no good arguments at all. They're aware it's ridiculous to feel sullen about whatever it is, but they do anyway, and find themselves unable to let go as quickly as they might have wished. Thankfully, I'm blessed with a wife who's more balanced and emotionally mature than I am. Calmly, with a subtle hint of humour, she said: 'Björn, that mantra you were talking about yesterday, maybe this would be a good time to use it?'

And there I was, on the other side of our breakfast eggs, with the stubborn bottom lip of that four-year-old stuck out as far as it would go, muttering: 'No, I use a different mantra now – *you may be wrong.*'

I'm being slightly facetious, of course. And I can understand if people have reservations and feel the mantra is too simplistic. But maintaining that kind of humble perspective is not easy, let me tell you. Especially in the heat of the moment! Is there a single ego on this planet that finds it easy and natural to say: '*I may be wrong*'?

No.

Do we as humans have access to something bigger, that is always fully aware it *may* be wrong?

Absolutely.

Imagine what the world could look like if most people, for the most part, remembered that they might be wrong. Imagine what conversations would be like.

Eight hundred years ago, Persian Sufi master Rumi said: 'Out beyond ideas of wrongdoing and rightdoing, there is a field. I'll meet you there.' I feel reasonably convinced more and more of us yearn for that field, and those meetings.

I remember one time, later on in my monastic life, when I had moved to a monastery in England and was bickering with someone about something. Our wonderful abbot Ajahn Sucitto looked at me and said: 'Being right is never the point.'

Of course! It's just so deeply ingrained in us! But none of us is required to be good at things without practice. Everyone has the right to try things out. And we're naturally inclined to try things that improve our wellbeing. And as it happens, few things are a better guarantor of that wellbeing than slowly but surely getting used to the idea that I may be wrong, maybe I don't know everything.

We like to think we understand what's going on, that we can accurately interpret events and the world around us. That we know. That we can decide and determine whether things are right or wrong, good or bad. We tend to think life should be the way we want it to be, the way we planned. But often, things don't turn out that way. In fact, they rarely do. And there's wisdom in not expecting life to turn out the way we think or feel it ought to. There's wisdom in understanding that we are essentially clueless.

FOURTEEN

Maybe, maybe not

One of my favourite stories is a Chinese fairy tale. It was first told to me by our English abbot Ajahn Jayasaro, during another night of meditation. As usual, a lot of people had come to the monastery to take part. From both the nearby villages and further afield. I should mention at this point that Ajahn Jayasaro had become very popular in Thailand. He donned his monk robes at a very young age and had already been a monk for ten years when I joined our monastery. He was probably only five or six years older than me, but by that point he'd earned considerable renown and respect in our world. He'd written some well-received books about Buddhism, was a popular meditation leader and had become known to the wider public because he sometimes appeared on TV.

Ajahn Jayasaro was a particular favourite among the staff of Thai Airways. Several of them had flown up that night from Bangkok; they would meditate with us all night and then take the morning flight back to work the next morning. Try to picture it: twenty-five or thirty monks, all of a sexually active age and celibate. *Really* celibate. We were lined up on a knee-high platform along one side of the meditation hall. On the floor diagonally in front of us, eight or ten *really attractive* flight attendants from Thai Airways were sitting in the lotus position, looking harmonious.

I, still fighting sleep, couldn't help but think that I wouldn't half mind checking out those flight attends. Just a little. Of course, my next thought scolded me: *Seriously, Björn. You're supposed to be a monk. You can't be checking out girls when you're supposed to me meditating, get it together!* But I kept arguing with myself, insisting it wasn't really me who wanted to check them out. *It's, like, biology or something, whatever it is that ensures the survival of the species, that brought us here from the savannas of Africa at the dawn of humanity. It's something positive, vital, there's nothing wrong with it. Buddhism is great at not shaming people for basic biological urges. No worries. Completely natural! And so maybe if I just take a really quick peek, no one will notice?*

I allowed myself a microsecond's glance in the flight attendants' direction. It felt watertight. *No one can have seen. Maybe I can afford an ever so slightly longer look?*

Time seemed to crawl as the meditation session continued. Many of the congregants were sitting straight-backed with alert yet calm postures. I was desperately fighting sleep. Among other things, I put a sewing needle between my thumb and forefinger to help me stay alert and awake. The idea was that it would wake me if I started drifting off and my muscles started relaxing. But, no, when that pinprick came, I slept right through it. Eventually, my inability to stay awake made me so desperate that I decided to switch to walking meditation instead. I usually did better with that. I moved over to the back of the hall, only to discover that I was perfectly capable of falling asleep on my feet, too. Waking up because your knees have buckled and you're about to hit the ground is a decidedly unpleasant feeling.

But I wasn't the only one. A few other unhappy souls experienced the same problem. One of them, an American monk, was at least as desperate as me. He went so far as to fetch a length of cloth from his hut. When he returned, he went over to one of the columns at the back of the hall and threw his cloth around a wall-mounted fan sitting some way up it. He grabbed the hanging part of the cloth and tied a small loop, which he put his head through so that he could continue his standing meditation without falling down.

One of my favourites among our regular congregants was a lovely, dignified woman. She was over eighty years old. Laywoman though she was, she never missed an all-night meditation. Her hair was always pulled back into a large, silvery bun and she had a round, kind face that just glowed. She looked like she was halfway to heaven. Very beautiful. Impressively, she always made it through the whole night and never looked rigid even though her back was as straight as a broomstick.

At one point that night, the woman left the meditation hall to use the bathroom, passing us on her way out. When she returned, she studied us briefly. Then she walked right up to the abbot at the front of the hall and knelt down in front of him. As it's considered impolite to disturb someone who's meditating, this was highly unusual. But she did it anyway, and said quietly: 'Forgive me, I'm so sorry to disturb you, but I have to, because I think the American monk in the back is about to kill himself.'

Around midnight, the novices brought in the hot drinks. The coffee made me feel slightly more awake. After that, it was finally time for our teacher to give his lecture. This is similar to a Sunday sermon in the Christian tradition and a lot of us really looked forward to it. I was no exception. Ajahn Jayasaro was an incredible role model and inspiration to me. As soon as he started speaking, I wished the whole world would stop, be quiet. I didn't want to miss a word.

Ajahn Jayasaro launched confidently into his lecture. Normally, English was the working language in the monastery, but since a lot of locals attended the all-night meditations, these particular lectures had to be given in Thai. Ajahn Jayasaro had truly mastered the language and

I often used his lectures to practise my own Thai. Since he was English, he spoke slightly slower and more clearly than the natives.

On this particular night, Ajahn Jayasaro told us something that sounded a bit like a fairy tale, an old story from China. He described a small Chinese village in which lived a very wise man and his adult son. The two of them had a very chatty neighbour.

The wise man and his son owned a small farm, consisting of a handful of rice paddies. To help with the farming, they had a draught horse. One day the horse escaped from its pasture and ran into the woods. The chatty neighbour stuck his nose over the fence and lamented:

'Oh no! Yesterday, you had a horse, and now you don't! How are you going to run your farm without a single draught animal? What bad luck!'

The wise farmer replied with an expression that in Thai takes the form *Mai nae*. It means something like '*who is to say*'. I like to translate it as '*maybe, maybe not*'.

A few days later, the horse returned from the woods of its own accord and brought with it two wild horses. All three happily walked through the gate to the pasture. The farmer closed the gate behind them and noticed his chatty neighbour poking his nose in again:

'Oh! Yesterday you had no draught animals at all and today you have three horses – how lucky!'

The wise farmer calmly replied:

'*Mai nae.* Maybe, maybe not.'

After a while, it was time to tame the wild horses, to break them in. The farmer's son set to the task. But before long, he fell off one of the horses and broke his leg. The chatty neighbour again:

'Oh no! Your only son, the only person you have to help out on your farm. Now that his leg is broken he won't be of any use in the fields anymore. How unlucky!'

The farmer replied: 'Maybe, maybe not.'

A short time later, the imperial army's pennants were seen snapping in the wind beyond the crests of the surrounding hills. The army was marching towards the village. Conflict had broken out on the Mongolian border and all men of fighting age were pressganged into joining the army to fight the Mongols. Except for the farmer's son, of course, since he had a broken leg. He was allowed to stay in the village. Once again, the chatty neighbour popped up and said:

'Imagine! Everyone else lost their sons, and many are surely destined never to return. But you got to keep your son. How lucky!'

The farmer: 'Maybe, maybe not.'

The farmer doesn't believe it's possible to know whether things that happen in life are good or bad. Loosening our grip on those types of convictions is both liberating and a sign of wisdom. There's a lot to be gained from remembering just how little we really know about the future, from objectively separating what we *believe* from what we *know*. I've rarely heard anyone say: 'Everything turned out exactly the way I thought it would.' On the contrary, for my part at least, I would have to concede that most of the things I've worried about in my life, never happened. And most of the things that did happen, I could never have seen coming.

FIFTEEN

Ghosts, asceticism and grief

In the forest tradition, monks and nuns try as best as they can to live their lives in a forest or jungle. At the same time, they rely entirely on other people for the food they need, which means they can't settle too far from civilisation. As a consequence, most monasteries are found near one or more villages. A particularly suitable location is what's commonly referred to as the cremation grove, since the forest around them is often well maintained and cared for. Our monastery was built by just such a grove.

A cremation grove is the place where regular Thai villages burn their dead. Once or several times a month, the villagers bring a large open casket and place it on a mound built just for this purpose. A fire is lit underneath the casket and then they watch as the body burns. I have witnessed this many times and it has helped to make death a relatively natural, mindful part of life.

In addition to their beautiful setting, cremation groves make for suitable locations for monasteries because many Thais are almost comically afraid of ghosts, which guarantees monastery residents a degree of seclusion. The villagers believe ghosts appear in, or often just hang around, cremation groves. So most of them are afraid to go near them, especially at night.

I remember once when we were travelling away from the scorching heat of north-east Thailand to the cooler highland jungle on the Burmese border, as we did every February. Our bus stopped in a village outside Kanchanaburi, where the villagers were anxiously awaiting us. It turns out blood-curdling screams were keeping them awake at night, and these particular ghosts were screaming in English. Apparently, there was a mass grave dating from the Second World War in the village. In it lay many Allied soldiers, who had died as prisoners of war while building the 'railway of death' and the bridge over the River Kwai. We – about twenty forest monks, most of us westerners – went to stand in a circle on the mass grave. We sang a number of the Buddha's reflections and traditional blessings, all in the liturgical language Pali. Then our abbot, Ajahn Jayasaro, addressed the ghosts directly in English: 'We come in peace. You're scaring the villagers with your screaming at night. You're dead now. There's nothing here for you. It's time to move on. Go in peace.'

For some reason, that was all that was needed. It worked. The ghosts stopped screaming and the villagers could go on living their lives and we could live ours.

I've never felt more part of nature than during the two months we spent in the highland jungle every year. When the bus couldn't go any further, we hiked the last part of the way, which took us a couple of days. A group of Burmese guest workers had made us bamboo cots in the jungle. They were well spread out, so we couldn't see or hear each other when we were on them.

At night, the mosquito net was the only thing between me and the jungle. I could hear the patter of insect legs against the flimsy roof, the chirping of the crickets, unidentified rustling in the leaves. Sometimes, I felt like a meatball on a plate as I sat there meditating. Just waiting for someone or something to come and gobble me up.

A Dutch monk ran into two tigers down by the river one night. Luckily, they'd already fed. But it goes without saying he was terrified and ran away as fast as his legs would carry him. There were quite a few jokes about 'the flying dutchman' after that. I heard something big crashing around one night but simply turned over and went back to sleep. The next morning, the ground by the bend in the river, no more than twenty yards from my cot, was covered with elephant tracks.

One day in the highland jungle, after our daily meal, we were asked to help move a giant brass Buddha statue. It needed to be brought to the top of a hill, where a small pagoda had been built. Someone had a Land Rover with a winch. Someone else had put down logs to roll the statue on. The Burmese got stuck in. The Thai rolled up their sleeves. And many of the monks helped, too, while a handful of us westerners backed away from the commotion. Stood back and pointed. We suggested ways the task could be completed more quickly and with less effort. Our abbot Ajahn Jayasaro put a hand on my shoulder and said: 'Natthiko. The important thing here is not how efficiently we do this, but how we all feel afterwards.'

In the mornings we would walk down the mountain to do a quick alms round in the valley. Gibbons sang their drawn-out song in the canopy and the half-tame hornbill was already waiting for our leftovers. The village was poor, so our daily meals were very basic during these periods. Sometimes, it was little more than rice, bananas and maybe some tinned sardines. In many ways life was even more extreme than back at the monastery, and never before had I been forced to face myself so relentlessly. It gave me experiences that have enriched my life ever since.

I chose to spend my second year as a monk as the only westerner in a very poor forest monastery on the

Cambodian border. From time to time, we'd hear mines exploding in the distance. Usually, it was a cow or goat that had triggered them.

Ajahn Chah once said: *Being a forest monk is about trying to let go, and to fail at it ninety per cent of the time.* I was reminded of this day after day, not least at mealtimes. After the alms round, when all the main courses had been handed over to Ajahn Banjong, he would pour everything into a big bucket. Pieces of buffalo meat (with hairs still sticking to them) were mixed in with chicken satay and sundried fish. 'Pah, food is medicine. It's good for young monks to let go of your food preferences,' Ajahn Banjong always insisted.

As I'm sure you can understand, I ended up eating a lot of fruit that year.

During the three-month monsoon season, we focused on meditation even more than usual. Ajahn Banjong decided that we should all place a box of matches on our heads during morning mediation. Anyone who let it fall off more than twice would get nothing but rice to eat that day. For a notorious sleepyhead like myself, this was, needless to say, a serious challenge. But I was given more than rice in my bowl every day but one that monsoon period. And, sure, it helped a little that I glued a coarse piece of cloth onto one side of my box of matches and learned to sleep with my torso leaning forward but my chin still up.

During my fourth year as a monk, I was once again invited to spend a year in a monastery with no other westerners. I leaped at the opportunity. This monastery was located near Bangkok Airport. When the monastery was first founded, there was nothing but rice paddies all around it, but by the time I arrived, ten years later, the monastery was surrounded by suburbs. From my simple hut, I could see straight into the kitchen of the nearest terraced house. Right into the refrigerator, as a matter of fact, whenever someone opened it. The frosty Singha beers looked particularly tempting.

Over the course of this year, a hard and wordless sorrow was growing steadily stronger inside my chest. I couldn't understand why or what it was about. I tried to let myself feel it. I tried to accept it, talk to it. I tried to be patient with it. But nothing seemed to help. It was just lodged there in my chest, sucking the joy out of my life.

One afternoon, after we'd had tea, I felt I'd reached breaking point. I couldn't go on as I was. It felt like I was never going to be happy again. So I walked back to my tiny hut, carefully hung up my outer robe, lit some incense and knelt down in front of my bronze Buddha. I put the palms of my hands together in front of my chest and tersely, but with intense feeling, told the Buddha statue: 'I can't do this. This is bigger than me. I feel completely helpless. Help me.' Then I began to bow. Again and again.

Slowly, slowly, the sorrow began to shift. I didn't resist, just let it take me over. My eyes filled with tears. Hesitantly at first, then more forcefully. My body was moaning, shaking, sobbing. But I just kept bowing. After a while, my tears slowed and I realised a part of me was calm and curious, aware of this explosion of anguish. Then my tears dried up completely and I looked around, as if with fresh eyes. Everything had regained some of the shimmer I'd experienced that morning so long ago, in my grandparents' house in Karlskrona. Awareness returned. I felt calm. It filled me with awe that this encounter with my own helplessness was the key that once more opened the door to joy.

SIXTEEN

Self-inflicted psychological suffering

Most of the psychological suffering we humans experience is *voluntary* and *self-inflicted*. That was one of the Buddha's greatest discoveries. It's a stage of human development we can't skip; we all go through it and it's entirely natural. And that's exactly what I keep coming back to – that we believe in thoughts that want to harm us. Thoughts that make it hard, heavy and complicated to be you and me.

Somewhere inside, whether consciously or subconsciously, we know a lot of the things that are difficult in our lives are caused by our own thoughts. Our psychological suffering is for the most part not caused by external events but, rather, by what's happening *inside* us – the thoughts bubbling up that we can either believe or not. It's there, in our minds, that our suffering is created; that's where it lives and thrives. For as long as we allow it to.

The fact that psychological suffering is self-inflicted doesn't make it any less painful. Not at all. But understanding that it is can give us a new way of relating to it. I would argue that's the main reason you shouldn't believe your every thought.

Such an insight can be difficult because it requires quite a lot of humility. We can no longer afford to blame other people or circumstances. But it also piques our interest: how can I relate to my own thoughts and feelings in a way that doesn't create so much psychological suffering for myself?

One level of the human psyche is very fond of blaming others for everything: 'If my parents had been different, if the people at work hadn't been so mean to me, if the politicians could just make better decisions.' There's nothing we can do about that; it's a fundamental aspect of our ego. Exceedingly natural. When life gets hard, when we face psychological pressure, pointing fingers is easier and leaves us less vulnerable. But even if it makes us uncomfortable, it eventually becomes completely necessary to ask ourselves the question: is there anything I can do, right here, right now, to help me feel less awful in this situation?

The world will keep on turning. No one else, nothing else, needs to change to make it easier to be you and me. Because when we feel under pressure, sad, lonely, anxious, small and inadequate, those feelings are remarkably often caused by some thought we're clinging to, stubbornly refusing to let go. Often, it's a perfectly reasonable thought. And it often contains a 'should'. *'Dad shouldn't have done that. Mum shouldn't have said that. My friends should have remembered. My children should have cared. My boss should have known. My partner should say, be, think differently.'*

And the thought that hurts the most – I should be different. I should be wiser, more hardworking, richer, better, thinner, more mature. You can be stuck in that groove forever.

But you can also gently step out of it. And with a smile on your lips say:

Thanks for your input. We'll get back to you.

SEVENTEEN

How many Pepsis can a hermit drink?

During my seventh and last year in Thailand, I lived as a hermit. Mum and Dad came to visit in February as usual and together we travelled to a national park in Chanthaburi province, where they accompanied me up a mountain. A twenty-minute walk brought us to the hut that was going to be my home for the next twelve months – a dilapidated, rotting, leaking, monsoon-damaged bamboo hut in the middle of the jungle. Sixty-five square feet with a ceiling so low I could barely stand up straight. Dad looked sceptical. But being an unusually wise father, he said nothing.

That afternoon we made our way back to my parents' hotel room. I relished every moment of the first hot shower I'd had in two years. Then it was time for me to set off for my first night in my new home. A storm had just blown in over Thailand, and the power went out in the hotel just before I left. When I reached the jungle at the foot of the mountain, it was almost completely dark. It was pouring with rain. For some reason, my torch refused to turn on. All around me I heard the wind tearing at the trees and the crashing of big, dead limbs falling to the ground. I realised the ground must be alive with snakes, as terrified as me. So I cleared my throat and set off down the barely visible jungle path one step at a time, belting out verses to protect against snakes, taught to us by the Buddha.

The walk, which earlier in the day had taken us twenty minutes, now took me nearly an hour, but in the end I reached my hut. Wet and covered in scratches. Excited and calm at the same time. I lit the candle next to the Buddha statue and bowed.

Six months into my stay, one of the men from the village just below the national park where I lived died. We had got to know and like each other when I, once or twice a month, ate my daily meal down in the village and tried to share my understanding of Buddhism in stumbling Thai. In his will, the man had set aside a princely sum to upgrade my hermitage. One of his final wishes had been to give visiting monks and nuns a better hut to live in. His gift made me very happy. I hope it made him even happier.

I was allowed to design the new hut myself. The biggest luxuries were the mosquito nets on the windows, the standing height inside and a covered path, ten paces long, outside for walking meditations.

In the forest tradition, monks shave their heads twice a month: when the moon's new and when it's full. Usually, monks shave each other, but, as a hermit, I obviously had to do it myself. By happy accident, Mum and Dad had just given me a hanging toiletry kit, so I would hang it up on a branch above the brook and attach a small mirror with Velcro fasteners to the unfolded kit. I would squat down at the edge of the brook and lather up my scalp, then pull out my razor and shave.

On this one particular occasion, I spent longer than normal contemplating my reflection. As usual, it had been two weeks since I had last seen it, and I studied my face with critically. I've never liked the large pores on my cheeks and nose. Or my blotchy, uneven skin that's still marked by the spots that plagued my youth. I would have liked smoother, more even skin, like the Thai. And my nose – wasn't it ridiculously hooked right at the tip?

As you can see, I had a lot of time on my hands during this period. Time for my own thoughts. And as I was sitting there, critically studying my face, something inside me whispered: '*That's odd ... I feel a lot more beautiful than I look.*' Right. Inner beauty. I'd lived an unimpeachably ethical life for seven years at that point. I hadn't deliberately hurt so much as an ant. Not done or said anything that weighed on my conscience. Through meditation, I'd become a more mindful person. And I'd worked to bring out in myself many of humanity's most beautiful inherent characteristics: generosity, empathy, patience, compassion. I'd become more beautiful on the inside.

At the foot of the mountain where my hermit hut was located there was a small village. It had only a single street. The villagers who gave me food every day during my alms round became my friends, of course. After a while, a curious dance developed between us; they tried to work out what I liked to eat, while I tried to be a good forest monk by not expressing any preferences: '*Alai godai* – anything is welcome!' was all I would tell them, in that uniquely Thai tone I'd learned to like so much.

After each meal, I washed my alms bowl in the lagoon by my hut. I gave the fish my leftovers. Went for a swim. Then I let the small waterfall massage my back while tiny fish ate the dead skin off my feet and legs.

That was probably the happiest year of my life. I still don't fully understand why. Maybe it's true what my teacher Ajahn Jayasaro wrote on the postcard he sent me that year: '*It seems to me, the more refined forms of happiness are characterised by the absence of things, rather than the presence of things.*'

Days turned into weeks, weeks into months and months into a full year. Slowly, a decision was formed. It was time for me to go back to Europe, for the first time in seven years. I'd heard about a monastery in the south of England that belonged to the forest tradition. They had a very wise teacher there – and nuns! Besides, I've always been a bit of an anglophile, so England felt like a natural choice. And the proximity to my family obviously didn't hurt, either.

When my year as a hermit came to an end, I decided to make one last pilgrimage before returning to Europe. It felt like a nice and meaningful note on which to end my stay in Thailand. And so I walked the three hundred miles back to my home monastery as a gesture of gratitude for everything that had been and as a gift to my teacher.

The trek was not without its challenges. Three hundred miles with everything I owned on my back. In plastic sandals. With no money at all. I simply had to trust that I would meet decent people along the way.

Contrary to what you might be imagining, I didn't walk through verdant forests and beautiful jungles. Most forests have been cut down, even in Thailand. And many of those that remain are monocultures, which makes them difficult to navigate. So for the most part I walked along roads. On most days, around a dozen cars would stop and a typical exchange might have sounded something like this:

'Wow, cool, someone who's living like in the good old days. Can we help you, can we give you a ride to somewhere?'

'No, thank you, I have promised myself to walk the whole way.'

'Can we give you some money?'

'No, I'm a forest monk, we don't use money.'

'Okay, but surely there's something we can do? Can we give you some food at least?'

'No, I'm sorry. As I'm sure you know, we only eat one meal a day in the forest tradition, and I've already had mine.'

'But, please, something, isn't there anything we can do for you?'

'Well ... maybe a Pepsi?'

So I kept walking, mile after mile, with eight or ten Pepsis in my bloodstream, wondering whether this was really what the Buddha was referring to when he talked about the holy way of life. A few days into my trek, it started to rain hard. I took shelter in a small grocery shop by the road. It had an earthen floor and I found a fizzy drinks crate to sit on. The people inside and around the shop were in a tizzy. In those parts, seeing a western forest monk was unusual. They started asking me all kinds of questions:

'How long have you been a monk?'

'For seven years now.'

'Okay. How long have you studied?'

'Well, I suppose it was sixteen years, in all.'

'How many siblings do you have?'

'I have three brothers.'

After a while, I realised there was a pattern to their questions. For one thing, all my answers were written down, and, for another, all the answers were numerical. There was something odd about the whole thing. Then I understood: *the next lottery draw's tomorrow!* There's a widespread belief among the Thai that meditating forest monks and nuns have a connection to the supernatural.

The rain stopped half an hour later and I was able to continue my journey. After a while, I met a lovely old man dressed all in white. I could never quite get used to the veneration with which the Thai would often greet us monks, and it seemed even more absurd when it came from older people. This day was no different. The old man approached me and said: 'Oh, it's a deep honour for me to meet an honourable, respectable forest monk. Has the honourable forest monk had any interesting dreams lately? Were there perchance any numbers in any of them?'

What a delightful mixture of reverence and self-interest!

At a later stage of my journey, I met a handsome young man on a motorcycle. He pulled over when he saw me and we struck up a conversation.

'Wow! A western forest monk, I've never met one of you before! I'll take you anywhere you want to go!'

'Thank you, but the thing is that this is kind of like spiritual training for me. I've made a promise not to enter any vehicle, but to walk the whole way back to my monastery.'

'Sure, but look, I've done some stupid things lately. I need a bit of good karma. Can't you just let me take you to the next village?'

'Sorry, I can't. I'd be breaking my promise.'

At that, he looked at me and said:

'Isn't that a bit selfish?'

I just smiled. But he was determined:

'Come on. A hundred yards? How bad can it be, can't you just let me give you a ride for a hundred yards?'

'No, I'm sorry, that would mean breaking my promise to myself ...'

He was quiet for a bit and then said:

'But could you give it some gas at least?'

'Absolutely!'

I walked over to his motorcycle, grabbed the accelerator and revved the engine for a minute or two.

'Thanks! Bye!'

That was one version of Thai street Buddhism.

EIGHTEEN

Closed fist, open palm

After seven years in Thailand, I was a bit sick of living with only men. There were vanishingly few nuns in the monasteries there. Unfortunately, what's true of most world religions is also true of Buddhism: women simply don't have the same opportunities as men. Things may be slightly better in the Buddhist tradition than in some other denominations, but they're still far from good. The cynical part of me suspects all the big world religions exist in part to keep women down. That is deeply tragic.

As it spread across the world, the Buddhist forest tradition I belonged to had, as I've mentioned, established an order for nuns. Its headquarters was located in England where a new monastery had also been founded. It wasn't perfect, but it was good enough. I'd met some of those nuns (and monks from the same monastery) when they visited Thailand, and I liked them very much. For monks and nuns to live side by side felt rewarding and in many ways natural to me. It brings a certain sense of balance when male and female are allowed to coexist on equal terms. So part of the reason I relocated to England was this, possibly slightly un-monkish fondness I had for nuns.

Several of the nuns in England came to be wonderful and important friends of mine. One of them was Ajahn Thaniya, a New Zealander of tiny stature but extraordinarily powerful character. She was one of the three most insightful people I've ever met. She didn't even need to ask how I was doing; one look at me was enough for her to know.

Another thing that drew me to this particular English monastery was that the abbot there was a monk who'd completely bowled me over – Ajahn Sucitto. He was the author and illustrator of a book which provided what I felt was an absolutely brilliant analysis of the Buddha's first lecture. We had got to know each other in Thailand, as he often travelled there in the winter. To this day, he remains one of my closest and most important friends.

Ajahn Sucitto has that thing really good teachers, mentors or for that matter friends should have – an infallible sense of timing. He was always able to say the right words to the right person at the right time, and he always served up his lessons with a large helping of love. Accepting wisdom from a person like that is easy, even when what they say touches a nerve.

In England I was happy to discover, we were served both breakfast *and* lunch. I was very grateful for this. I recall one of the monastery breakfasts particularly vividly. It took place relatively soon after I moved in. There were more than fifty of us – monks, nuns and guests – who had eaten together and after much debating we had managed to decide who was going to do what that day. It got very involved because there were a lot of things to sort out: who's going to cook, who's going to do the washing up, who's going to mow the lawn, who's going to tend to the flowers, drive the sick nun to the hospital, drive the monk to the dentist, fix the tractor, fetch the firewood, chop the firewood and fill the boiler?

The chaotic nature of it bothered me. I felt the English monastery was a bit rough around the edges in general. I'd come from the *original* monastery in Thailand. I knew how things were done in a *real* forest monastery! In England, things were a bit sloppy and disorganised and, as a serious forest monk, I certainly *wasn't* okay with it. So I stayed behind when the others got up, thinking annoyed thoughts about how this behaviour was unworthy of a forest monastery, that things weren't being done in the proper way, that proceedings should have been more polished and mindful. People shuffled out of the room and, in the end, the only two people left were my teacher Ajahn Sucitto and me. At that moment, I may well have had one of the tightest sphincters in all of West Sussex.

Ajahn Sucitto gave me a gentle look and said: 'Natthiko, Natthiko. Chaos may rattle you, but order can kill you.'

Right. I was clenching my fist too hard again. I was imagining I knew what the world should look like. And when it didn't conform to my ideas, I seized up. Thoughts with the word 'should' in them make me small, dull and lonely.

If you can relate to that feeling, try practising this hand movement – clench your fist hard, then let it unfold into an open hand. I hope you can carry that with you as a reminder. I often use that gesture during my lectures and meditations because it epitomises so much of what I'm trying to communicate. It's simple, but it's a good illustration of how we can let go of things we cling to too hard: things, feelings, convictions. Clench your fist hard, then relax it into an open hand.

I hope you can your live life with slightly less firmly clenched fists and slightly more open hands. Slightly less control. Slightly more trust. Slightly less I need to know everything beforehand. Slightly more take life as it comes. It does all of us a world of good. Life doesn't have be lived with constant anxiety about things not turning out the way we want. We don't have to make ourselves smaller than we are. We have a choice. Do we want to grab life by the throat or do we want to embrace it?

Relax that fist as often as you can.

NINETEEN

Get a fucking job, mate

Living as a Buddhist monk in a country that isn't suffused with Buddhist tradition is obviously a very different experience. When we did our daily alms rounds in Thailand, we were always greeted warmly, almost admiringly, by the locals. We held respected positions in society. In the UK, it was a different story altogether.

I did my first alms round in England with a young English monk named Narado. With our alms bowls around our necks, we wandered onto the high street in Midhurst, the small town nearest our monastery in West Sussex. I was nervous, couldn't quite come to grips with the idea that people would actually give us food, even in England. A white van drove past. The driver rolled down his window and shouted: 'Get a fucking job, mate!'

It was a pretty clear reminder of the different ways monks are viewed. For seven years, the Thai had more or less treated me as gift from the gods. Monk. Forest monk.

Western forest monk! That's about as fancy as you can get in Thailand. In England, I was seen as something more akin to a parasite. A suspect person with terrible taste in clothes, a weird haircut and confused sexual orientation.

I'd obviously never taken the Thai expressions of reverence personally. And that was lucky for me. Because during my time as a monk in the west, where insults were hurled at me from time to time, they genuinely passed right through me. I felt like a cartoon character who sees a bullet coming at him, then sees it whizz through his body and come out the other side. That was another gift from the Buddha: I was learning how to handle both praise and criticism wisely.

In fact, the incident with the white-van man gave me a wonderful sense of freedom. It really brought into focus how mindful I had become when he shouted that insult. I, who have always been so sensitive to what others think of me, could now listen to what was happening inside me and calmly note: *nothing*. What a relief! That moment really brought it home to me that I was no longer living a life that revolved around amassing impressive merits or looking good to others. I finally felt free of that.

The way I see it, genuine human, spiritual and transcendent growth isn't so much about learning coping strategies; it's more about putting down our baggage. About learning how to get stuck in our hang-ups a little bit less often and for shorter periods of time. Forget about not having hang-ups. Only the dead have no hang-ups.

If, as you work on self-improvement, you notice that your hang-ups are slowly fading, you know you're on the right path. Maybe you're even able to create a healthy distance from what your personality is like, from what you yourself think you are and all the opinions you may have about your personal shortcomings.

For me, it was an exhilarating feeling when the me who existed beyond my inadequacies started to come into view. Despite my incoherent, overreactive, overly impulsive, unbalanced personality, I can now see that as I become better at listening inwardly, as I work on making the stillness my own, something has begun to shimmer. Something that always seems to be with me. Something that wishes me well.

TWENTY

Don't forget to leave room for miracles

In the forest tradition, ten years as a monk or nun earns you the title Ajahn, the Thai word for teacher, at which point you're encouraged to try your hand at teaching. I remember the first weekend retreat I was asked to lead in England. The night before, it was as if two snakes were wrestling in my stomach. The anxiety was almost unbearable. Just before the retreat was set to begin, I went into the meditation hall, lit candles and incense, bowed to the Buddha statue and said quietly: 'Okay, Buddha. I'm a wreck right now. But I'm going to be completely present all weekend. I know the words won't be coming from me but *through* me. Deal?' I took the Buddha statue's silence as agreement. The retreat went well.

This was a period when I felt overwrought and increasingly tense. I had to practise intently and frequently to genuinely move from that closed fist to the open hand. With more and more administrative duties ending up on my table, a certain amount of stress had also entered my life. Who knew there were stressed monks! And as we do know, stress has a tendency to make letting go of one's need for control even harder. No matter who you are.

Ajahn Thaniya noticed, of course. One evening in June, we were both heading into the meditation hall for a group meditation. The spring air was clear, the lily pond in the monastery garden was full of dragonflies that sparkled as they hovered just above the surface of the water. Ajahn Thaniya looked at me in that special way of hers. I loved it when she did that because, soon after, she would almost always say something terse and cryptic, something valuable. So it made me prick up my ears when she looked at me with her warm eyes and said: 'Natthiko, don't forget to leave room for miracles.'

It struck a chord in me, because I knew how true it was. And I really needed that reminder at that moment. Right. I'm walking around trying to control everything. That makes life lonely, tough, fraught, and anxious. Trust life a bit more! Almost all the best things in my life have been outside my control, I know this. Trying to direct and predict everything just makes life hard. Not fun. I lose a part of my intelligence when I get this tense.

I've long been a disciple of an American teacher by the name of Adyashanti. I went on my first retreat with him nine months after I left monastic life. It was a profound experience for me. I was in the presence of greatness

— that's what it felt like — and I hung on his every word during the seven days the retreat lasted. One night he said something I've carried with me ever since.

I still remember the exact moment very clearly.

Adyashanti said: 'Listen, if you don't unquestioningly believe everything you think, if you're completely mindful (and only when you are), if your attention is unfettered, you will discover a fundamental truth. That the universe operates according to this principle:

> You will know
> what you need to know
> when you need to know it.'

Wow. I obviously can't prove, beyond all doubt, that this is the case. And I get it if it sounds hippy-dippy, but I have absolutely no objections to Adyashanti's statement. I feel it is in every respect true, and I've lived by it for a long time now.

I've noticed that my life is always better, sometimes a lot better, when I manage to live by that principle. That obviously doesn't mean being reckless with your life. It doesn't mean you shouldn't plan when planning is possible and appropriate. But it does mean we can reach a higher plane of both freedom and wisdom if we get used to living with more trust. When we're able and brave enough to let go of our vain attempts to control and anticipate the future. Then, something almost magical happens.

You might say, simplifying things slightly, that there are two kinds of thoughts that dominate almost all humans: thoughts revolving around our own history and thoughts revolving around our own future. These thoughts are mesmerising, and they all have the same fingerprints: my life.

It's as though you're walking through life lugging these two big, heavy, important bags with you – one containing all your thoughts about your history, the other all your thoughts about your future. They're wonderful, valuable bags. But try putting them down, just for a bit. See if you can greet some part of life more immediately, here and now. And if you're successful, you can pick the bags back up later. If you want to.

There's nothing wrong with thinking about your own life. But there's value in taking a break from it from time to time. Let it rest, let it sit. That usually makes it easier to pick the bags up again.

Everything's connected: letting go of your thoughts and of control, turning inward and listening, being present, regularly resting in what's peaceful, living in trust. All of it is about exploring the possibility of finding something that's *more real* than our thoughts, more valuable than our thoughts. To some degree, we turn back towards the place from which the thoughts bubble forth. And the strange thing is that, once we do that, our thoughts become more valuable. We gain better access to our wise and intuitive side. It may sound harsh, but the *quality* of our thoughts improves.

Let's examine the interesting word *future* a bit more, and the fact that we have thoughts about what is going to happen in it. There's much to gain from being very cautious about what you think about your future. But what your head tells you about the future isn't the future. It's a sketch, a fragmented picture based on your memories and experiences. And you only remember a fraction of what actually happened in your life. What's more, your memories are strongly shaped and determined by emotion.

We're programmed to remember things that were emotionally accentuated, not least those things that were hard and painful. It's natural, because it helped our ancestors to survive and procreate on the savanna. But what we call the past isn't what *actually* happened. It's fragments, often cherry-picked from emotionally charged situations. And *those* then provide the basis for what we project onto our future, what we use as the foundation for how we imagine life will be. But that's *not* the future. That's supposition on our part. That's speculation about how things may potentially, maybe, hypothetically, possibly turn out. No one knows for sure. No one.

TWENTY-ONE

Only one thing is certain

After a few years in the English monastery, my monk friend Narado and I decided to hike around the Isle of Wight. It was early summer. We were one day into our journey and had walked twenty miles along the spectacular north coast of the island and camped for the night under a majestic oak tree. It was late morning and time for our first alms round on the island. We put our backpacks down against the wall of a cemetery in the seaside town of Sandown, hung our alms bowls around our necks and took up position on the high street, a stone's throw from the supermarket.

We stood there for an hour. A thousand people must have passed by. No one spoke to us. A little girl asked her mum if she thought we might have snakes in our bowls. We tried standing near a hair salon instead, but it was the same. People barely dignified us with a glance. It was as though we were invisible, despite our golden ochre monk robes. After a while, a police car pulled up to us and a policeman climbed out: 'Boys, begging is illegal on the Isle of Wight. Besides, the hair salon has called in a complaint. You're scaring away their customers with your haircuts.'

I explained to him that we weren't begging. We weren't asking anyone for anything. We were open to the giving of alms. That's not the same thing. 'Fine, but move it along,' the policeman replied firmly.

We returned to the spot by the supermarket. My legs were shaking with exhaustion and hunger after our hike and twenty-four-hour fast. Since we followed the rules of the forest tradition, we were only allowed to eat before midday, but in the western world, where daylight saving is a factor, 1 p.m. had been set as the limit. It was now 12.30. I told my monk companion we were probably going to have to give up until the next day: 'We can handle another day of fasting. We'll try again tomorrow.' As I said the words, I felt a kind of release inside. The clenched fist of hunger relaxed into the open palm of acceptance. But my friend wasn't ready to give up yet: 'Let's just give it a bit longer,' he said. I consented.

Not a minute later, an older woman with a kind face walked up to us: 'What are you boys up to?' I told her we were Buddhist monks, and open to alms. 'Aha, so you want food, you mean? The Isle of Wight is a Christian island. No one goes hungry here. So, what would you like, then?' I explained that we gratefully accepted anything that was ready to eat, that it was part of our training to let go of our preferences. 'Oh no you don't. If you want me to spend my hard-earned cash on you, I want to buy you something you'll enjoy.' My monk friend had a soft spot for a certain type of northern English pies, so I mentioned them. The woman nodded and went into the shop.

Not long after, a handsome couple approached us. They turned out to be Canadians. The man told us the porter at their hotel apparently lived near our monastery in the off-season, and that he had explained to them who we were and what we did. They asked us to hold on a minute and disappeared into the supermarket as well. Five minutes later, we were standing there with four carrier bags full of food. We thanked them, sung a short blessing and then rushed back to the cemetery. There, we sat down on the grass and ate in silence. When we were done, I stayed where I was, resting in stillness for a moment. I remembered my teachers in Thailand telling me: 'You won't always have what you want, but you'll always have what you need.' That was exactly right. And, strangely enough – whenever I relax my hold on my desires, they seem to be fulfilled more easily. May I never forget that lesson.

Among the nuns in the English monastery was one called Ajahn Anandabodhi. She was a colourful character, raised in the north of England. When she first came to the monastery, she had a tall mohawk dyed every colour of the rainbow. Ajahn Anandabodhi and I joined the monastery around the same time and, after a while, we were both tasked with dealing with the many practical things that needed to be solved in our community.

As I mentioned before, this made me extra busy for a while and I was noticeably stressed. I planned the physical labour in the monastery, greeted guests, answered emails and the phone and generally dealt with a lot of the administrative work. Simply put, I was something akin to a monastery CEO. I had slipped back into my role as an economist, which wasn't really what I wanted from my monastic life. Ajahn Anandabodhi noticed that I was tired and overworked. One evening at teatime we passed each other in the hall between the kitchen and the tearoom. She stopped me and reminded me: 'Natthiko. Don't forget: responsibility – the ability to respond.'

What helps us respond to life as it unfolds? Well, it's like I've said before: often its less about planning, control and organisation than you might think, and more about presence. Everyone knows what it feels like to be in the flow. You're alert and attentive. Aware, if you like. You don't dwell anxiously on the things that might go wrong, wondering how to respond to all conceivable and inconceivable outcomes. You're not constantly worried about things turning out the way you want them to. Instead, you're mindful enough to respond in an open manner. Which is also, as a rule, by default a wiser plan of action.

Letting go of our need for control, being aware, is a lot about mustering the courage to face uncertainty. Most of us find that challenging. Human beings want to know. It's natural and we all have that urge. When we don't know, when things are uncertain, we often feel frightened and become inflexible. So we pretend that things are more predictable than they really are, even though we actually live with enormous uncertainty all the time. We cling to our plans and ideas about how things should be and turn out ever so desperately. And there's nothing wrong with having plans. It's wonderful, we all need to plan our lives to some extent. I think it's a beautiful thing. But there's a difference between planning and thinking all your plans have to come to fruition.

American president Eisenhower once said: *Planning is everything, plans are nothing.*'

Imagine if we all used pencil instead of ink to write in our calendars and planners. Both figuratively and literally. Imagine if we could bear in mind that what we write down, what we think is going to happen, might not be what actually happens. And if we could try our best to be all right with that.

A big part of spiritual growth is about finding the courage to face uncertainty. When we learn to endure not knowing and not being in control, we gain access to a wiser part of ourselves. Trying to cling to life is like trying to cling to water. It's in its nature to be in constant flux.

Monastic life was designed to frustrate the mechanisms we employ to exert control. That was one of the reasons we didn't handle money, weren't allowed to choose when or what we ate, who we lived with or which hut we slept in. Being forced to relinquish control was a deliberate part of the learning process. And the result was wonderful. It's a gift to be able to rest in trust when life becomes uncertain, to be comfortable with not knowing.

It's about doing less legwork. About being less firmly rooted in what we think we know, about the future, for example, as I've just mentioned, and more open to the here and now, which is the only place where life really happens.

If we're being completely honest, we know full well that every human life contains endless uncertainty. There's only one thing we know for sure in this life, and that's that it will end one day. The rest is hopes, fears, assumptions, wishes, ideas and intentions. We might as well admit it and accept it. Relax that clenched fist and let your open hand be filled with life.

TWENTY-TWO

'Hips Don't Lie'

After seven years in the English convent, I moved to another monastery within the forest tradition, this time to Kandersteg, a village in the Swiss Alps. Apart from its proximity to the mountains, which I had always been so fond of, this monastery came with the added benefit that I no longer had to serve as the 'monastery CEO'. The Swiss were eminently capable of running the organisation; no one does that better. I was free to look after our guests, to be available to people who needed support and to hike and climb the mountains. I also spent more time teaching meditation and slowly found my own voice in that area.

Our abbot and my closest friend there, Ajahn Kemasiri, was like a father figure to me, and he loved football. He had escaped the German Democratic Republic at the age of twelve, in the middle of the night, together with his family. As a young man, he'd run a sourdough bakery but by the time we met he'd been a dedicated monk for many years. My close friend Carl-Henrik hit the nail on the head when, during a visit to the monastery, he described Ajahn Kemasiri as a submarine captain – just like the archetypal male leader in the classic German film *Das Boot*!

By this time, I was leading meditation retreats in half a dozen countries and Ajahn Kemasiri was probably wondering just how Buddhist they really were. He heard from the participants that I often talked about *The Truman Show*, *The Matrix*, Winnie-the-Pooh and the Moomins. But, luckily, he knew as well as I did that the Buddha was completely uninterested in dogma and fundamentalism. We both viewed Buddhism as the world's most wonderful toolbox.

In Switzerland, monastic life was less strict than in the other monasteries I'd lived in, particularly those in Thailand. Here, we were entrusted with more freedom. The monastery was so modern it even had an internet connection. Once I learned how to google, I simply *had* to look up myself. One of the first hits my name generated back then, in 2006, was a PDF from a conference in Malaysia I'd attended in the early nineties, when I was working for the UN's World Food Programme. The title I was given in that document is the only reason I hope I may one day compile a CV again. In the document, I was introduced as an 'international expert on the financial analysis of small-scale seaweed cultivation'. Beat that!

Mum and Dad gave me a computer. Someone else had presented me with an MP3 player so that I could listen to recorded lectures. When Carl-Henrik, my best friend from home, found out about this, he was thrilled and immediately sent me a CD compilation titled 'The 100 top songs since you became a monk'. An unforgettable gift.

To my great joy, in Switzerland one day a week was dedicated to hiking. My unreserved love of the mountains meant I always walked twice as far and climbed twice as high as anyone else in the monastery.

One day, I set out on one of those hikes – I put on my boots and slowly made my way up a spectacular saddle point, from which I could see all the way down to the capital, Bern. It was spring and just starting to get warmer, though there was still a lot of snow in the mountains. With that magnificent vista spread out before me, I settled down to eat the food I'd brought. It tasted heavenly.

The sun was hot, so I removed a layer of clothing. Then another. I've always liked basking in the sun. Eventually, I was wearing nothing but my skirt and my boots. Then I popped the headphones of my MP3 player into my ears and selected the playlist 'The top 100 songs since you became a monk'. It wasn't long before Shakira's 'Hips Don't Lie' came on and I could no longer sit still. The Bernese Oberland's stiffest hips slowly began to sway.

TWENTY-THREE

But I'm the monk who never doubted

I was sitting in my small room in the beautiful monastery in Kandersteg. I was drinking a cup of tea and reading something inspirational. Then I lit my incense stick and my candle and settled down to meditate. After twenty years of daily meditation, I'd reached a point where I no longer dozed off; I'd actually started to enjoy meditating, almost unreservedly.

So there I sat, in front of my gilded wooden Buddha, resting in awareness. One breath at a time. Everything slowly grew still. Not stillness as in the absence of activity, but stillness as in presence. A stillness I'm used to by now, and awfully fond of. It has become my home, a place I can rest. My body became accessible and I felt very alive and content. It was an amazing feeling and I just wanted things to stay that way. That continued for maybe ten or twelve minutes. Then that deep, wise, insightful voice of intuition spoke to me again. Something inside me whispered: It's time to move on.

Oh no! How inconvenient! My life was so good the way it was.

I was very surprised. And frightened. But I'm the monk who's supposed to die in my robes. I'm the monk who never doubted. And suddenly, at the age of forty-six, I discovered something inside me telling me it was time to go home. The voice was as clear as on that Sunday in May on my sofa in Spain, twenty years before. I obviously knew I couldn't ignore it. But I had so much to lose. My entire life and identity was entwined with my monastic existence.

So I took my time, maybe six months. When I called my mum to tell her about my decision, she said thoughtfully: 'Sure, I suppose you are a bit young to retire.' She'd visited me in the Swiss monastery and probably felt it seemed a bit too like an old people's home. There was something to that. My life as a monk had become too safe and predictable. I'd been doing it for so long and knew my role so well I was almost running on autopilot.

One thing that I didn't factor into my decision to stop being a monk in any real way, but that nevertheless impacted my life around this time, was that I had developed an unusual autoimmune disease called ITP. Between leading two retreats in South Africa, I'd hiked the mountains in the KwaZulu province, and something had bitten me on the leg. It didn't start hurting badly until a few hours later, but soon after my blood lost the ability to coagulate properly.

When I went to A&E in England two weeks later, the doctor said: 'You're a ticking time bomb.' ITP is considered a serious illness because the blood platelets are prematurely destroyed, which can cause severe and sometimes even fatal bleeding. Back in Switzerland, I underwent several intensive treatments, without success. The doctors wanted to remove my spleen, but I refused. Instead, I was put on very high doses of cortisone for a while, which made me sleep very poorly. My body has never fully regained its ability to enter deep sleep.

Even though I had already made my decision to leave, the process was a difficult one. I spoke to a lot of former monks and nuns. By this time, I knew more former than active monks and nuns. It is common not to stay in the monastery your whole life, but, rather, only for as long as you want to and it feels right. Most of the people I'd lived with during my many years as a monk had given up monastic life – disrobed – before me. And all the former monks and nuns told me the same thing: *You have no idea how confusing it is and how much it hurts to step out of it now that you've lived it for so long. The larger part of your identity is based on this. Who will you be out there? It's a lot harder than you can ever imagine.*

I had no trouble believing them. But I took the plunge anyway. I knew it was the brave thing to do. I figured the trust capital I'd built up practising facing uncertainty should stand me in good stead now; it was now time to cash it in and spread my wings in a harsher reality.

Somewhere along the way I picked up an expression that really speaks to me and that I often use when I lead meditations:

We learn in stillness, so we remember when the storm comes.

That's one of the reasons people attend retreats or spend time meditating. To practise. You can't live your life in a meditation hall. But when we're novices, when we haven't mastered something yet, then favourable circumstances are good to have. A place where we can practise in peace and quiet so that we are then able to step out into the less predictable climate of the everyday more sure-footed. Because, of course, all the things we learn should work in ordinary life, too. If they don't, what are they really worth?

Life will inevitably throw storms my way. Again and again. Sometimes, I'll be a lone ship adrift in rough seas with no lighthouse or beacon in sight. Sometimes the turbulence will be milder, but still unpleasant – my boss yelling about something I should have done last week, a conflict with someone I care about. Then, my attention will probably be drawn to whatever is screaming the loudest inside me. But if during calmer periods I seized the opportunity to learn to let go of thoughts, practised the ability to choose where I direct my attention, then I have an infallible ally. A partner who will stand by me in every situation, who is always on my side.

TWENTY-FOUR

Farewell letter

In October 2008, I sent a letter to my monk and nun friends in various monasteries, telling them about my decision. It went like this:

Dear Ones,

It's been a long time since I wrote one of these letters to you all. Many of you know that my health challenge remains. I've been through an extensive array of therapies and treatments since last summer, both conventional and alternative. I've tried virtually everything. The problem with my blood not being able to coagulate seems difficult to cure and is likely something I'm going to have to learn to live with. Subjectively, the other symptoms are quite bearable, insomnia being the most inconvenient one. Energy levels are lower, of course, both in body and in mind, but it's been instructive for me to learn to live with less vitality. I certainly feel a lot more sympathy for folks with energy problems now!

The main reason I have not been writing for so long is that in October last year, something inside urged me to consider whether I want to remain a Buddhist monk. It surprised me, since I've never before had any real doubts about this. The intellect was rather baffled, pointing out the inconvenience and uncertainty of getting a lay life together at 46, especially with the present health issue. I tried to ignore this urge, but it kept returning. By April, it turned into a clear conviction that I need to disrobe. Still, I was reluctant to act. This conviction reasserted itself in early May again, and again in late June. I realise this all sounds a bit mysterious, almost as if the impulse originated from somewhere other than 'me'. But that's how I've experienced it.

So I'm sceptical about presenting reasons, since this intuition definitely preceded reasons. One image that conveys well how I feel is that of a garment you've used for a long time. One day you notice it doesn't quite fit anymore. Nothing wrong with it, but it's time for a change.

The time has come to lead a different life, as a lay person. I believe it will do me good to stand on my own two feet, and make my own decisions, this being the first one.

I also feel that some of the constrictions of life as a monk are not helpful for me personally any longer, and that a bit more freedom in choosing my responses to life is needed. I have no worries that my spiritual health will suffer, the enthusiasm for awakening is very much alive. On the level of physical health, I´m hoping lay life will bring improvements, and I know there are promising developments in conventional medicine and, if I get an opportunity, I might try them, but it's not a major factor in my decision.

I've consulted my spiritual mentors, and talked to my family, my brothers at Dhammapala and a few other monks and friends about my decision. As always, I'm reminded of how many good and wise friends there are in my life. I have a hunch this will continue, it seems to be my greatest talent! The decision is mine alone, of course, and is obviously not the one most of my mentors favoured.

Workwise, it's still pretty vague. The illness means I won't be able to work full-time anytime soon, there's just not the juice for that. Somehow I don't worry too much about livelihood, I'm sure it will become clearer what's next as time goes by. Initially, I'll just have to take pretty much anything on offer, and that's fine. Over time, I wouldn't be surprised if opportunities arise to share what I've learned over the years in the Sangha.

Overall, there is a reassuring albeit irrational sense that 'everything will work out fine'. That sense includes even the vague but recurring premonition that this body might not last a 'normal' life span.

I find it hard to know what to include and what not to include in a letter such as this. I trust there will be time to talk things over with many of you in Switzerland and England over the coming period. I will be travelling around for about a month before I return home. The theme for this period I imagine will be to honour what's been, clumsily try to express the inexpressible gratitude, and try to survive the grief of separation.

In case anyone wonders, I'm not in love, and there's not a particular woman on my mind. Yes, I do wish that the male/female divide in our communities didn't cause so much pain and confusion, but living here in Switzerland I'm less affected by it. I could go on. And, yes, there are times when the notion of a romantic relationship seems very appealing, but I long ago stopped believing that someone else can, or should, make me happy and fulfilled forever.

My parents and my three brothers seem very happy to have me live a bit closer and more accessible, and my youngest brother is already sorting through his wardrobe for clothes to pass on. He's in the fashion business, so I fear I'll look more hip than I'll feel ...

I notice the words aren't quite falling into place. Partly it's the lack of proper rest, partly it's the fear of sounding flippant. Being sober and serious isn't really my natural mode. It's important for me to try to acknowledge all that's been given to me over the past 16 years, although I know that's impossible. The guidance, the friendships, the encouragement, the material support, the travels, the fun, the opportunity to learn, grow and let go in safe and supportive environments, and much more.

There are moments when gratitude catches me from behind, and it's almost too much to bear. Through all this support and encouragement, it has become a lot easier to be me than it was 16 years ago. Mind you, I do prefer not getting too serious about being me, and that is getting a lot easier too!

So, one phase is coming to an end, and something else begins. I'll carry the blessings of my years as a monk with me until my last breath, and beyond, I imagine.

With love, grief and gratitude, all mixed up together,

Natthiko

When it was time for me to leave the monastery, a beautiful and heartfelt ceremony was held in the meditation hall with those closest to me. Halfway through the ceremony, I went to my room. I took off my robes for the last time and pulled on a pair of jeans for the first time in seventeen years. Then I went back to the meditation hall and returned my robes to Ajahn Khemasiri. He chuckled and said I'm the best-dressed ex-monk he's seen in his twenty-two years in robes. Dressed in this unfamiliar shell, I left the harbour and set my course for the open sea.

TWENTY-FIVE

Darkness

I got back to Sweden in November 2008. And despite all the love and thoughtfulness my family and friends showed me, I quickly sank into depression. I'd listened carefully to the former monks and nuns who had warned me about the pain and grief of no longer living in that kind of community. And yet, I felt completely unprepared when it hit me. The force of the blow was unbelievable! And my illness obviously didn't help, either.

My close friend Pip's mum had generously allowed me to rent her guest cottage for a token sum. So there I sat, in a tiny cabin in the countryside outside Knäred, southern Sweden. In the dark of winter. Alone. Depressed. Sleepless. Sick. With no job or money. And I wasn't exactly cheered when my first pension statement arrived in the post. Or when I travelled into the nearest town, Laholm, to apply for financial assistance. I was asked first to register as a jobseeker. At the employment office, I filled out all the forms and met with a caseworker. He looked at my CV and said: 'Well, this looks great up until 1989 ... That's twenty years ago.'

'I know.'

My application for financial assistance was rejected. Thankfully, Mum and Dad supported me not just emotionally but financially as well, for as long as I needed. I hadn't handled money once in seventeen years and came home to a society where money was unbelievably central to life. I caught myself thinking: '*How do people do it? How do they find the money to live, eat, dress, take the bus, maybe even go on holiday from time to time?*' I was shocked at how expensive everything was.

It wasn't long before I was clinically depressed. I woke up almost every night, in a bed sopping with sweat, because anxiety was churning in my chest, in the pit of my stomach. Severe anxiety. We throw that word around quite a lot these days. But I'm obviously not talking about your regular, workaday anxiety. I'm talking about an utterly abject anxiety, where you're so irretrievably stuck in apprehension and fear that it's like a trance. I'm talking about a filter that seems to strain all the joy out of life. A curtain falling across all thought. Something whispering in the background, ceaselessly, relentlessly: *It's going to be like this forever. It will never get better.*

Anyone who has ever experienced true anxiety knows that if you believe your thoughts at those moments, things can turn dangerous. There's no limit to how dark things can get. Or how quickly. Having something toxic in your mind that's constantly trying to convince you things will never get better is deeply unsettling and one of the greatest psychological horrors a person can experience. You may have ten lovely, empathetic friends who keep telling you it will pass, who keep reminding you of all the other things that eventually changed – of course this will, too, one day. You hear them, you comprehend their words. But nothing happens below your chin. Down there, the dark voice is still whispering.

I don't think I've ever been through anything as horrible as that period. Eventually, things got so dark that one night I got all practical and considered whether I should simply end my life. Granted, it was just a thought, but it was there. Clear. I couldn't bear to feel anymore, I couldn't understand how I was supposed to be able to carry that weight any longer. And I want any of you who have a loved one who's feeling down, or if you are yourselves going through a period so dark it almost takes your breath away, to know that. You're not alone. A lot of us have been there. And turned it around.

It's easy to withdraw when you're feeling that bad. To isolate yourself like I did. It's rarely helpful. Maybe never. We begin to exist in the presence of others. That is extra important when things get hard. If you can, be with people who reflect your light. Try to find strength in relationships that feel safe and easy, where you feel liked for who you are.

Months passed. Another winter came. Almost all my friends had stopped calling, because I never answered, and when I did I was curt and didn't want to make plans to meet up. I couldn't bear to talk to them because I felt like I was going to infect them with my darkness. I could feel I was coming to the end of my tether. Night after night, I changed my sheets. Lay down on my back, but didn't dare to fall asleep, because that instantly brought the bad thoughts back:

I'm never going to have a girlfriend, never going to have a family, I'm never going to find a job or be able to afford a house or a car. No one is ever going to want to be with me. I've spent seventeen years working on my spiritual growth and this is what I have to show for it.

I felt ashamed a lot of the time. I had dedicated half my life to deepening, understanding and developing myself as a person. I should have come home a tiny ball of timeless, shining wisdom. Instead, I felt like one of the unhappiest people in Sweden, one of the biggest failures. The only sound in my head was the bellowing of my thoughts about the future: *Everything's just going to get worse.* I couldn't resist or argue with them. It was like bringing a wooden sword and a tiny helmet made of newspaper to a fight a fire-breathing dragon.

That anxiety was the least forgiving and best spiritual teacher I've ever known.

I've never been as motivated not to believe my every thought. Because even though the pitch-black thoughts were frighteningly convincing, all those things I'd learned and practised still provided the flimsiest of lifelines. In spite of all the darkness inside and around me, I could, through meditation, find a place to rest. Breathing space. Because I'd practised letting go for so long, I could call on that ability in my moments of deepest despondence. Not always, but often enough, I managed to turn my attention from those horrible thoughts to my breathing. Granted, they would stubbornly return again after a single breath, but after working on it for a while, I got to a point where I sometimes managed two consecutive breaths. It helped me pull through.

It was eighteen months before I could see the light again.

TWENTY-SIX

This too shall pass

What I wanted more than anything was to shut myself up in my cottage, hide from everyone and everything. My idea of a good day was when no one called or emailed me, so I could binge-watch another half-season of *Desperate Housewives* all alone. But thankfully, the world refused to respect my isolation. And I did realise, too, that it wouldn't end well if I just kept to myself and said no to everything that came my way.

Dad was wise enough to say, after a year and a half: 'Look, Björn, you're too passive. That ten thousand kronor we've been giving you every month as an advance on your inheritance, that's done now.' I obviously didn't like his decision, but I knew he was right. So I slowly started to poke my head out of my burrow. During a visit to the monastery in Switzerland, my monk friend Ajahn Khemasiri told me, kindly but firmly: 'Natthiko, it's time to share yourself again.' And he was right.

I started teaching, shorter and longer meditation retreats. It went surprisingly well. Back then, most meditation teachers in Sweden were foreign and taught in English, so there was demand for someone who could do it in Swedish, and I was appreciated. Doing something that someone else valued was like a balm for my soul, and I started to conquer myself again, one step at a time. I had something to contribute.

My teaching helped me finally to find a place that could be mine. Sharing with others what was so close to my heart felt deeply meaningful – a feeling I hadn't had in eighteen months. That the people I met welcomed me with a noticeable degree of appreciation meant a great deal as well. And to once more be in situations where people told me about themselves and their lives, where I could once again offer my full attention, and sometimes my support and encouragement – how I had hungered for such meetings!

After a while, I dared to take the next step: to speak to people who hadn't sought out retreats or some such. My friend Daniel invited me to speak to the tenants of his office hotel, Arkipelagen; after that I increasingly and more frequently gave lectures to private companies and government agencies. And I was stunned at how appreciated I was there, too. Who knew I had something to contribute after all! Despite the psychological wounds

I carried. Despite the confusion and depression. Despite the anxiety.

My confidence and self-worth were still shaky, but slowly but surely I started to feel that maybe the labour market did have a place for me after all. People looked like they were okay with listening to me for a while. A lot of them even told me they found it valuable.

Being welcomed by such a kind and generous world made all the difference. It may sound too religious for some of you, but I state it firmly – I think of it as karma. After all, I had spent the last seventeen years learning to listen more and more to my most beautiful inner voice. And it had an effect. Now, the world wished me well.

In the middle of all this, I got a call from Sweden's public broadcaster SVT: 'Stina Dabrowski interviewed you back when you were living in a Thai monastery, right? Okay, so, her husband's a producer for *Summer Evening with Anne Lundberg*. Why don't you come on the show and tell us what it's like to be back and what your life is like now!' My entire being howled inwardly: '*Noooo, no, no! You think you're getting someone who will sit there and radiate timeless wisdom, but I'm still so deeply unhappy and confused.*' At the same time, I heard myself saying: 'Of course, I'd love to be on your show.' How did that even happen?

So in June 2010 I found myself in the studio. Towards the end of the interview, Anne asked if there was

anything I particularly looked forward to. I replied that
I was looking forward to falling in love. After we wrapped
up, Kjell Dabrowski hugged me and said: 'That was the
slickest lonely hearts ad I've ever seen!'

A couple of weeks later, before the show had even
aired, Elisabeth contacted me on Facebook. She's a friend
of a friend and we'd only met once, at a dinner party
twenty years previously. After connecting online, I invited
her down to Falsterbo, where I was living at the time.
Elisabeth had recently attended a workshop where the
leader had told her how much it had meant to him to
find a spiritual mentor. Elisabeth thought maybe I could
be her spiritual mentor? I had very different plans.

Elisabeth climbed out of her rental car in the car park
by Falsterbohus. We were both a bit shy but pretended
not to be. I had an angry sunburn from a day at the beach
and we laughed about that for a while. We took a bike
ride down to Skanör. Elisabeth talked quite a lot, and consequently swallowed a lot of insects. We laughed about
that for a while, too. It all felt unnaturally natural. I felt
like: *Of course it's the two of us. This is the woman I want by my side.
Come rain or shine.* I had a bottle of sparkling rosé chilling in
the fridge and my famous fish stew bubbling on the hob.
We ate in the garden. The swallows were flying high. And
my heart was, too.

Elisabeth became the best part of my life. She has
always been like medicine for me. Our physical closeness

and tenderness are medicine. Our shared every day, her grown-up children, are medicine. The food she cooks, her love and zest for life. Her humour, her laugh. The wisdom she embodies with every breath. Medicine. Like all lovers, we go through rough patches. We pick at each other's wounds, almost always without meaning to. But those broken, hurt places are exactly the ones that need to be brought out into the light of loving awareness. So everything is exactly as it should be. Even in those moments. Thankfully, we have both long since realised how futile it is to bicker about who's right and who's wrong, so we rarely get stuck in blame games. One time, I talked in my sleep, but addressing Elisabeth. She lay awake next to me, listening. In my dream, I called her The Gift. And that's exactly how I feel.

When Elisabeth and I decided to get married, I asked her blessing to put an unusual inscription in my wedding ring. She was happy to give it because she knew what the words meant to me. When the jeweller heard what I wanted, she laughed and said it was the most unromantic thing she'd ever been asked to inscribe in a ring.

The words I wanted in my ring I heard for the first time twenty-five years ago. One starry night in Thailand, our teacher Ajahn Jayasaro told us a story set in the Middle East in the thirteenth century. A Persian king ruled his realm with legendary wisdom. Among his subjects was a man who really wanted to know what lay behind the king's wise rule. The man wandered for weeks until he reached the king's palace, where he was finally granted an audience. When the man knelt before the king, he asked: 'What is the secret behind Your just, auspicious and celebrated way of ruling our country, honoured King?' The king took off his gold ring, gave it to the visitor and said: 'You will find my secret inside this ring.' The man held the inside of the ring up to the light and read aloud:

This too shall pass

Nothing lasts. Everything is impermanent. That's the bad news. But also the good news.

TWENTY-SEVEN

It starts with you

Love is one of the hardest subjects to talk about with sincerity. Love for others and love for oneself. It's a sensitive subject because it is so closely linked to what's most vulnerable in us humans. But that's also why it's so important.

The Buddha singled out four emotions he considered divine. They're called Brahmavihāra – dwelling of gods – because it's in these feelings the gods are found. It's also where the divinity in us humans is found. The beauty in us.

One of the divine emotions is *loving-kindness*.

One is *compassion*.

One is something we don't really have a good word for in the West: Mudita – humanity's inherent capacity to feel joy at our own and others' success. That feeling we have when someone we like is doing well, when they're happy. The closest translation might be empathetic joy.

The fourth is a bit out of left field: Upekkha. Equanimity is a common English translation. It's an emotion that contains a large measure of wisdom. Often, it's the basic emotional chord of awareness. Something tender. Wide-eyed. Awake. Something inside us that is capable of taking everything in and understanding that in this moment, things are the way they're meant to be.

In his instructions for how to grow in these divine virtues, these beautiful resting places in the human heart, the Buddha put it very plainly and simply: *You always have to start with yourself.*

Your compassion for others will always fall short and remain fragile, so long as you're unable to extend it to yourself first. In order to grow in our love, we need to be able to direct our tenderness inwards. Unfortunately, I think a lot of us overlook that, fail to make it a priority. We're often critical and hard on ourselves, failing to see that we, too, deserve compassion. Especially when we're not feeling well.

Wouldn't it be lovely if we could approach the things that hurt inside us with a bit more sensitivity, patience and empathy? Wouldn't it be valuable if we could meet our pain by genuinely and honestly asking ourselves the question: *'Is there any way I can help myself in this moment, so that I don't have to feel like this needlessly, and for too long? Is there anything I can do for myself to make it a little bit easier to be me?'*

We often find this challenging on an intellectual plane. It's far too easy to miss the quiet voice of our hearts when our heads are bellowing: 'I shouldn't feel this bad. I shouldn't react to this thing. I shouldn't be so easily riled, so easily hurt, so envious, so resentful.' But one thing's for sure – that kind of rebuke won't help anyone who's dealing with difficult emotions. Instead, we need to go to that place where it hurts and try to see it with as much compassion and understanding as we can muster. See if we can find a way to counter the dark thoughts and drag them out into the light, without believing their content.

If we can begin to see ourselves in a more forgiving, tolerant light, treating the people around us the same way follows naturally. But as long as we continue to view ourselves from a harsh and demanding perspective, we can't give others absolute love either.

We don't even have to use the word love if that feels too grand. One of my big monastic role models back in the day was Ajahn Sumedho – a large American, born the same year as my dad. He eventually settled on using the word non-aversion instead of love. It's not exactly gushing, but maybe it's a more realistic goal. Can I strengthen my capacity for non-aversion? To not dislike things. Things in myself and in others.

I know a lot of people whose compassion is hampered because they consider themselves deficient and inadequate. They don't consider themselves worthy of that emotional care. But if we're waiting until we feel worthy of love, until that feeling just magically appears, we risk having to wait forever.

What does it take for us to feel we deserve human warmth from ourselves? How good, beautiful and successful do we have to become? How long do we have to atone for our tiny mistakes? How immaculately do we have to do everything we put our hands to? Will we ever get there?

It would do all of us good to bear in mind that we're doing the best we can. Others are doing the best they can, too. Sometimes it can be hard to see or understand that at the time, but most of us want to do good, almost all the time. Sometimes, things don't turn out the way we wanted. Sometimes things come off well, sometimes they don't. But there's value in interpreting ourselves and the people around us with that in mind, that we're doing the best we can.

Only one of our relationships is truly lifelong, from our first breath to our last. The one we have with ourselves. Imagine if it was characterised by compassion and warmth. By an ability to forgive, to forget our little missteps. Imagine if we could look at ourselves with gentle, kind eyes and view our flaws with a sense of humour. Imagine if we could give ourselves the same loving care we give our children, or other people we love without reservation. It would do us a world of good. And the divine emotions in us would thrive.

TWENTY-EIGHT

Life in trousers

Back to the cottage in Knäred. I'd re-established a life of dignity and a new career was taking shape. But Sweden seemed harder to me than the country I remembered. The distance between people had grown. There was more stress. Everyone was talking about achievements and control. And I had been practising letting things go for seventeen years! What's more, I had discovered I infinitely preferred collaboration to competition, but that outlook was not a natural part of the society I'd come back to.

I remember meeting an old friend from the Stockholm School of Economics around this time. He asked what my business plan was now that I was working again. I replied that my business plan was to walk through the doors that opened for me. He wasn't particularly impressed. But for me it was a given, the only option, and it still is. Unless my intuition whispers *no*, then I listen to it.

And just look how things turned out. Suddenly I was guiding a hundred and fifty union members through a meditation on the mysteries of awareness. The next day, I shared my favourite magical mantra with eighty venture capitalists from all over the world. What a gift! I, who had always doubted I was good enough the way I was. I, who had never thought I had anything to contribute, never believed there was a place for me in the labour market where I could feel valuable and where I could share things that people might enjoy. And there I was being welcomed by a world that generously created one opportunity after another to do just that – through retreats, lectures, podcasts, TV and radio interviews, yes, even my own tour.

Things turned out the way I never dared to dream when I was at my lowest. Something inside me healed a little bit more each time I experienced that people actually felt I had something to give. And now, I look back at my career and just feel blown away, like after getting off a rollercoaster. *What a ride!*

It also seems to me a new kind of humility has begun to simmer in Sweden in the past few years. More people are open to turning inwards, to being less rigid, to testing out new perspectives and questioning their old ones. That bodes well for us.

My guiding star on my journey back to work was trust. It may be that it became more important than ever for me to mind the lessons about living life with open hands, about not always trying to manipulate circumstances to get my own way, and instead to trust the universe. There's obviously a big difference between doing that in my life as a Buddhist forest monk and in my life in trousers in a western society, but it's at least as important. Here, we tend to think we can and should control life more. But we're mistaken.

I remember one time, a couple of years after disrobing, when I was on my way to Mum and Dad's to return their car, which they had lent me since I didn't have one of my own yet. I'd needed it to drive to Hook's Manor, where I had been employed as the entertainment at the annual meeting of Sweden's golf administrators – one of many unlikely gigs for a former forest monk. As I approached Stockholm, my phone rang. It was from TV4. They wanted me to come on their morning show to talk about big life changes in the second half of life.

Apparently, they'd had a ninety-two-year-old on the day before who had just debuted as a crime writer, and it had proved a popular segment. I could just picture the brainstorming session at their team meeting: '*Do we have any other kind of old person who has made a big change late in life? Isn't there some dusty old ex-monk living down in Gothenburg? Maybe we could invite him?*'

I was stupid enough to say yes. Then my nerves kept me awake all night, of course. My self-image was still less than stellar and to say I felt tense about doing live TV for the first time is an understatement.

I made my way to the studio the next morning, nervous and shaky from lack of sleep. The hosts Peter Jihde and Tilde de Paula were extremely pleasant and after a while we sat down on the sofa and started to talk. The cameras were rolling. A little way into the conversation, I said something along the lines of: 'Sure, but, you know, sometimes one door closes in life and the next one hasn't opened yet. Something is less alive than it was – a relationship, a job, a home, the town you live in. It ends, and the next thing hasn't come along yet. Suddenly, you find yourself in a situation of heightened uncertainty. What do you have to lean on then? Isn't it valuable at those moments to feel an inherent sense of trust?

Peter Jidhe looked a bit like a kindly question mark. If he'd been a cartoon character with a thought bubble above his head, it might have said something like: '*I don't really get what you're talking about, but I dig you.*' Tilde de Paula's body language was considerably more sceptical. If she'd had a similar thought bubble, it would probably have said: '*Sure, fine, easy for him to talk about trust – free room and board for seventeen years.*' What she said was more polished, along the lines of: 'But seriously, Björn. People need day care for their kids, food on their tables, you can't always just rely on faith.'

I was prepared for that objection; I know it provokes people when I start talking about trust. But since I'd lain awake all night, worrying about this, I'd put some thought into what I would say. I replied: 'Absolutely, Tilde, you're right. I completely agree. Trust isn't always the answer or the solution. Some situations need to be controlled. Let's turn to the great, beautiful treasure trove of wisdom we call Islam. In Islam, there are many wise sayings, and one of these hadiths reads: *Trust in Allah, but tie your camel.*'

I wasn't being facetious, though the saying is funny. I love that wisdom, and I carry it with me. It's so easy to get stuck in either/or thinking, to get it into your head that you have to live in trust all the time and rely on nothing else. *No, no no!* When it comes to doing your taxes, for instance, trust is a terrible method. That's a place for control. When you need to be on time for some event you promised your children you'd be at, you'll probably want to do some planning. But my feeling is still that in this part of the world, in these times, more of us need to be reminded that trust is valuable.

For me, trust has come to be one of my best friends. When I'm trying to find the way forward in my life, trust and the intelligence of the moment are my twin compasses. I want to be able to trust myself, and I want to be able to trust life.

TWENTY-NINE

The meaning of life is to find your gift and give it away

Sometimes I almost get dizzy thinking about what life might have been like if I'd carried on working as an economist. I still remember the feeling of sitting there on the train, on my way to the AGA headquarters, the first six months after graduating from the Stockholm School of Economics. Every morning my thoughts were like a rowdy group of children in my head – jeering and pushing. They shouted at me about all the things I had to get done and achieve. And the constant undercurrent was that unrelenting nagging feeling of not having prepared enough, of not having thought everything through properly, of there still being tons of things that could go wrong. I sat there with a heavy feeling in my chest. *Is this what my work life is going to be like – never-ending anxiety about being under-prepared? Can't we just fast-forward to retirement then? What does it do to a person to spend so much of their time feeling this way?*

Thankfully, I found another way to start my days. A way that meant I wasn't stuck and lost in my own preferences, hopes and fears. That meant I could be aware of the fact that life is happening right here, right now. It's astoundingly more fun to live this way and it gives me deep joy to have been able to shape my current profession based on these foundations instead.

It all comes back to trust again, of course. When I give a lecture, for example, I don't use notes. I'm not saying there's anything wrong with notes. But I have a feeling that if I started to use a set script, and said the same thing every time, the things I had written down and rehearsed over and over, something inside me would wilt and wither. And I think my audience would sense it, too. It wouldn't be as 'real' that way.

One of the bravest things I've ever done workwise was going on a national tour in 2019. We called it *The Keys to Freedom*. It felt a bit cocky, but life had, more than ever, become too short to wait for the world's approval, so I just dived in. My friend and loyal sidekick Caroline tirelessly sorted out the practical aspects. Our plan was to visit eight or ten cities, but it ended up being forty before we were done. I've never felt so uplifted. For over twenty thousand people to be willing to give me such trust and open listening still feels unbelievable.

I asked some fellow public speakers beforehand: 'What do you think about a concept where a middle-age white man, with very understated body language, sits on stage for two hours and talks, without a script, intermission, music or visuals?' No one felt it was an obviously winning concept, which is highly understandable. The whole thing was really very eccentric. But it worked. Because even though there was no script or even a very clear plan, there was a very solid will and plenty of good intentions, and I've learned to trust those things. Besides, people seem to appreciate the sincerity.

Life back home in Sweden was starting to get into a pleasant groove, not exactly like the one in the monastery but a different kind: my everyday life with Elisabeth, the guided meditations and meditation weekends I was invited to lead, lectures to private companies, dinners with friends and travel to every part of the globe to visit monasteries and listen to my spiritual teachers. It wasn't the life I'd lived before becoming a monk. It wasn't the life I led as a monk. It was something new. And I noticed I had no major reservations. I liked it.

But there was a scratch in the groove. Subtle details that seemed unusual. Sleep continued to elude me. I fell asleep like a clubbed seal but often woke up far too early and was unable to go back to sleep.

During my runs, I noticed my body couldn't perform at its usual level. It was as if I was weakening at an increasingly rapid pace, losing muscle strength. One day, I realised I couldn't do push-ups or crunches anymore.

Something was wrong. Something in my body was telling me to pay attention.

One night in bed as Elisabeth and I lay next to each other reading, she suddenly looked up at me and asked why my body was twitching.

I put my book down and could clearly see the muscles in my chest, stomach and arms twitching and I couldn't stop it. It wasn't an earthquake, it was tiny tremors. Fasciculations.

I picked up my phone and started researching the bodily changes I'd noticed. The results weren't exactly uplifting.

THIRTY

Trust will get you there

My best friend in Thailand was called Tejapañño. We had
shaved our heads and become novices at the same time.
Tejapañño was one of those guys who is all heart. He was
from New Zealand, an old surfing champion, and one
of the most beautiful men I'd ever seen. On our alms
rounds, I walked ahead of him since I became a novice
one minute before he did. As tradition dictates, it was
usually the female villagers who brought out the alms and
when they put the food in my bowl, they lowered their
eyes and bowed slightly, palms pressed together. When
they put food in Tejapañño's bowl, they often glanced
up and fired off their most dazzling smiles. I couldn't
blame them.

Talking about trust brings to mind a journey Tejapañño
and I undertook. We were going to Malaysia to renew our
visas. Once you're a fully-fledged monk, the Department
of Religion in Bangkok takes care of that, but while you're

a novice you have to sort it out yourself. Even though we forest monks didn't usually handle money, the monastery was by no means lacking in funds. It had a foundation to which more than enough money was always being donated. So when our abbot whispered to the board that two novices needed train tickets to Malaysia to renew their visas at the Thai consulate in Penang, it was seen to.

We took the overnight train to Bangkok and the next morning a group of sweet old ladies were waiting on the platform to give us food. That afternoon, we reached Butterworth, on the mainland across from the island Penang.

The ferry across the sound cost a few ringgit. Now what were we supposed to do? As I've mentioned before, Buddhist monks and nuns aren't allowed to ask for anything.

We looked at each other and laughingly agreed this would be a great opportunity to practise patience and trust. So we took up position in the ferry terminal, at a respectable distance from the ticket window. We stood there for a few hours. People passing would stop and chat with us from time to time and eventually a young American man approached us:

'Hey, cool, western monks!'

'Hello!'

'Your robes are different from the orange ones I've seen in Bangkok, yours are a bit more ochre, are you forest monks?'

'Yes, we are.'

'What are you doing here?'

'Ehm ... well, we ... we're standing here ...'

'Sure, but this is a ferry terminal, right? Seems like an unusual place for forest monks to hang out. Shouldn't you be in, you know, the forest?'

'Yep, normally, we would be ...'

'I was just talking to someone who told me about forest monks. Is it true you're trying to live almost exactly like people lived in the time of the Buddha?'

'Yes, absolutely, that's right.'

'Is it true you don't ever handle money?'

'Yes, that's correct.'

'And yet, here you are?'

'Yep ...'

'Could it be you're hoping to catch the ferry, but you can't buy tickets?'

'There is truth to that.'

'Oh my God, that makes sense! I'll help you out. It's practically free anyway. Let me buy you two return tickets. I'm on it!'

When you read about monasteries, nuns, monks, rules and mossy old religions, I can't blame you if the first words you associate with them are control, predictability, constraint and seclusion. But I want you to know that wasn't at all how we lived. We were completely exposed and at the mercy of the generosity of strangers *every* day. Monastic life is designed to heighten the degree of uncertainty. And the results of that training are very useful.

It's confirmed to me again and again, even out in 'the normal world'. We don't live in a random, cold, hostile universe. Quite the opposite. What you send out into the world, that's what tends to come back to you. The more determined you are to control the circumstances of your life, the more uncomfortable you will feel when you're reminded that there's such a thing as trust. Which means you lose out on the benefits of that trust. And there might be situations where trust is the last thing left to lean on.

THIRTY-ONE

The news

It was pouring with rain in Varberg on 11 September 2018. When I stepped into the doctor's office in the hospital's neurology department, I felt like a soldier heading into battle. Collected and scared at the same time. As ready as a person can be for possibly having their world turned upside down.

After I started to notice my body behaving oddly, I went to the doctor. I underwent some very unpleasant tests that summer. One involved sticking a needle through my tongue. Another receiving hundreds of increasingly powerful electric shocks on various parts of my body. I obviously felt more and more convinced it was something serious. I'd googled my symptoms. I knew what the worst-case scenario was, and something in the pit of my stomach told me it was time to prepare myself for it. After a matter-of-fact presentation of my test results, it was as if the doctor took a moment to steel herself, and then she told me what she had hoped she would not have to: 'Björn, all signs point to ALS.'

Three little letters. ALS. The nightmare scenario. The disease the tabloids have nicknamed 'the Devil's disease'. The disease that makes your muscles wither away, until your body no longer has the strength to draw breath. Modern medicine has no cure for ALS, so it calls it incurable. I told the doctor I'd read on Wikipedia you usually have three to five years to live from the time of diagnosis. 'In your case, I believe it's more like *one* to five years,' she replied. As I write this, that was one year and nine months ago.

I slowly realised life was happening on two separate planes simultaneously. On a personal level, the news hit me full force. Despair and shock ripped through my innards. I was sobbing. At the same time, another part of me remained calm and faced this new reality with gentle, open eyes. Without resistance. Odd, but not unfamiliar. I still have that part of me to lean on – *awareness*. The part of me that's always awake, and never fights reality.

The doctor was good at her job and emotionally intelligent. She talked to me kindly and sensitively as I sat there thunderstruck. I tried to hold it together as best I could, since I wanted to record everything she was telling me on my phone, so as not to miss some important piece of information. She ran through what was going to happen next and then I left her office.

As soon as the door closed behind me, I fell apart. My body was shaking with grief when I called my friend Navid. My beloved Elisabeth and I had agreed not to relay the news over the phone, whatever it might be, but, rather, to wait until I got home. We were both so afraid of what it might be. So Navid kept me company through the soulless, endless hospital corridors, out into the pouring rain and into my car. Once behind the wheel, I felt I could handle the rest of the journey on my own, so we hung up. It went so-so.

I noticed the grief was crashing over me like waves. When I merged onto the motorway, volcanic eruptions of sadness racked my body again. I was overcome with unbearable thoughts like: '*I thought I was going to grow old with Elisabeth. I'd so been looking forward to having step-grandchildren and seeing them grow up.*'

So I called another friend, Lasse 'The Firefighter' Gustavson. Lasse is one of the most beautiful souls I've ever had the honour to meet. He's like a beacon of goodness in my life. Even on the stormiest seas, by the sharpest, most dangerous rocks, I can turn to him and find the light. And the light is always signalling the same thing, in the most convincing way: *Everything is as it should be. Always. The universe makes no mistakes.*

Lasse held my heart until I was seven or eight minutes from home and calm enough to get by unaided. I felt cried out for the moment. Emptied. The storm had passed and my body felt relaxed, my chest open. I was completely calm inside. I wasn't thinking about anything, just resting in serenity, experiencing absolute mindfulness.

Just as I was about to get off the motorway, something rose up inside me. That wise, intuitive voice spoke to me again, bubbling up from the same place it had several times before. It wasn't as rambling as what follows next, and I can't say it came out in actual words, more like an instantaneous vision or notion, but the message was very clear:

THANK you to all the powers involved, for encouraging me for so long to live my life with integrity. Thank you for providing such auspicious opportunities to bring out what's beautiful in me. Now that my last breath seems to be coming much sooner than I'd hoped, I can calmly take stock and say I've done nothing unforgiveable, nothing I deeply regret or haven't been able to put right. I have no heavy karmic baggage to weigh me down. When my time comes, when it's time to shuffle off this mortal coil for good, I'll be able to greet death with an open face knowing I've lived a good life. I'll be able to take my last breath without being afraid of what comes next.

It was a bit surprising, as magical moments tend to be. The feeling was immensely powerful and beautiful, almost joyful. And what's more, it was a confirmation. I've always known it's important to be decent and true, to live a life of integrity, guided by a clear moral compass. But at this moment, the way I experienced it, something wanted me to know that: 'You're well prepared for this, you're going to be able to meet death without regrets, there's no need to worry.'

THIRTY-TWO

Is this how it ends?

When I stepped into the hallway back home after driving all the way back from Varberg Hospital, I didn't have to say anything. Elisabeth knew, just from looking at me, that our worst fears had been realised. We fell into each other's arms and cried and cried. And it went on like that for a few days. Usually, we cried in shifts. It was as if our grief knew when the other had the capacity to hold and support.

On the third morning, I woke up early as usual and noted that my chest felt lighter. At around 6 a.m. a friend called, so I tiptoed into the laundry room and sat down on the tiled floor to talk, so as not to wake Elisabeth. After a while, she stuck her head in. I looked up. She smiled her soft velvety smile and mouthed a silent *Good morning*. We held each other's gaze for a long time. I noticed the light was finally back in her eyes. Hallelujah. No storm lasts forever. *This too shall pass.*

I eventually found a relatively open way of relating to the news of my sickness. It's hard to say if it was based on acceptance or denial. Maybe it doesn't matter. One way or another, Elisabeth and I managed to adopt an attitude that felt sustainable. Neither of us was willing to completely accept the doctors' bleak predictions as the only possible outcome. We wanted to leave the door open for a miracle. I might be dead before the end of the year, or we might have another twenty wonderful years together. No one knows for sure. *Maybe, maybe not.*

Once, I saw a sign that said: 'Don't give away things you wouldn't want yourself. Advice, for instance.'

When I made it known on social media I'd been diagnosed with ALS, I asked for people to keep their health tips to themselves. I obviously received loads anyway. I get it. It's a sign that people care. But there's a category of advice that I just don't understand why anyone would give, and it can be summed up like this: '*I know better than you why you have this disease. This is what you need to do to get well.*' Most of the explanations in that category revolved around there being emotional and psychological causes for my very physical illness. I can't tell you how much that pissed me off. So arrogant. So presumptuous. So unhelpful.

What was helpful, on the other hand, were the lessons I'd learned as a monk. After all, I'd spent seventeen years practising how not to think about the future, how not to believe my every thought. Those skills became more important than ever after my diagnosis. They helped me beat back the catastrophic thoughts a little, helped me not to obsess about what it would be like once I was in a wheelchair all the time, or when I couldn't speak or swallow anymore. Instead, I could sense something else growing within me: a very strong feeling of wanting to live until I die. I'm not afraid of death, I just don't feel ready to stop living.

It quickly became important to me to normalise my existence as best I could. I didn't want to *become* my diagnosis. It's so easy to make yourself a victim in situations like these, or an identity – '*the sick one*'. I've been careful to avoid that. Maybe that's part of the reason why I went on that tour after I was diagnosed. In a way, I wanted to remind the world and maybe myself 'I'm *still here, still around*'.

Not surprisingly, there are some practical obstacles to travelling by yourself with accelerating ALS symptoms. I had to dust off my rusty Thai to ask a hotel cleaner for help with buttoning my shirt and trousers. I had to practise trust when I was forced to ask for help to get my card back from the machine at a petrol station, or when I had to ask a stranger for a shoulder to lean on when I misjudged the distance from my hotel to the theatre in Linköping, or when I had to ask a young man to drag my suitcase across the cobblestones when I could no longer pick it up myself, or when I needed help after falling down in the middle of a street in Lund and hitting my head pretty badly. The list is endless. But as I require more and more practical help, it has also become increasingly clear: most of us like helping others. When a straightfor-ward opportunity to do so arises, we don't mind at all.

The following winter, just over a year after I was diagnosed, I suffered two severe bouts of pneumonia. The first one happened in Costa Rica over Christmas. In the end, it got so bad I had to be flown to a hospital in the capital. I remember lying there, looking out at the stars through the small windows of the Cessna, gasping for breath. 'Is this how it ends?' I wondered to myself.

Six weeks later, the pneumonia returned, but this time I was back home in Saltsjöbaden. One Saturday in February, my breathing became so laboured I called an ambulance at three in the morning. Even though it only took the ambulance ten minutes to get there, I had time to think that same thought: 'Is this how it ends?'

Both these episodes were incredibly frightening. But it wasn't the fact that it looked like my life was over that made me so scared. It was how it seemed to be ending. Suffocation is definitely not on my top ten list of ways to die.

I've obviously considered the possibility of doctor-assisted suicide in Switzerland if the ALS symptoms become too unbearable for too long. It's good to know that option exists. At the same time, something inside me increasingly just wants to let the natural process run its course. Like a good sea captain who chooses to go down with his ship, something inside me doesn't want to check out before it's time.

Since my diagnosis, my days have been filled with a good deal of grief, but almost no anger or rage. My grief is mostly about all the things that won't happen now, all the things I'm going to miss. The thought of not being there when my stepchildren have their own children hurts so much I still have a hard time talking about it without falling apart. And then there's the future I hoped to share with my wife. I want to grow old with Elisabeth so very badly.

But I've never felt angry at the ALS. Or God, or Fate. I was never promised a long life. We humans are like leaves on trees in that respect. Most leaves hold on until they're withered and brown, but some fall while they're still green.

THIRTY-THREE

Everything will be taken from you

Even though my psyche and my soul are still in good shape, it's obviously sad to feel my body gradually give up. Having ALS is a bit like being forced to live with a thief: first, there's the deeply unsettling moment the thief moves in. The equivalent to this in the world of ALS are the lumbar punctures, electromyography and neurography. Imagine a remarkably large needle, and a lot of smaller needles, in sensationally unpleasant places – often in conjunction with electric shocks and tests that last an unreasonably long time.

Then you slowly start noticing that things you've always had in your home have gone missing. The thief seems to have taken them. One day it's your ability to do a single abdominal crunch or push-up that vanishes. Another, your ability to run, swim, paddle, cycle, throw, hold or lift. You have to get used to asking for help to cut your nails, tie your laces, unlock doors, make a sandwich, buy petrol, open bottles, peel bananas, squeeze tooth-paste out of the tube. And a thousand other things.

Slowly but surely, you realise the thief won't be happy until he's taken everything from you. And that you – according to the best knowledge of the medical profession – can't do a thing about it. Thankfully, there's someone else in the house, too. My Elisabeth. And she happens to be a modern equivalent of a medieval knight in shining armour, who rides up alongside me in the heat of battle. She opens her visor, flashes her biggest smile at me and says: *'Don't be afraid. I'm here by your side all the way.'* Then you just know that however things turn out, it'll be okay.

I've lost forty-four pounds of muscle mass in two years. Every attempt to get up off the sofa is a feat of strength with uncertain outcome. Nothing physical – and I really mean *nothing* – is easy anymore. Not even drinking a cup of tea or brushing my teeth. And I have an electric toothbrush.

When Buddhists meditate, they mainly focus on being in their bodies, but there's a clear distinction: We *are not* bodies, we *have* bodies. The Buddha went so far as to say once that: 'Through this fathom-long body, I have sensed what was never born and never dies.'

The inherent nature of the body is to become sick from time to time, to age – if you're lucky – and one day to die. At some point during my Buddhist training,

I internalised a fairly realistic view of what can be asked of a human body. Sometimes I think of the body as a kind of spacesuit we've all been poured into. I was given this particular one. Mine wasn't as top-notch as some other people's, so it seems to have worn out a bit faster. That's not something I can control.

Without knowing it, my life as a monk in many ways prepared me for death. The Buddha emphatically stressed the value of remembering that we're all going to die one day, and within the forest tradition we took this very literally. We were exposed daily to the realisation that a human life is impermanent and will one day end.

When you entered the meditation hall in our monastery, the first thing you saw was a complete human skeleton in a display cabinet. The skull had a hole at the temple because it had belonged to a woman who shot herself. In her suicide note she left her body to the monastery, so that it could be used to remind everyone of our human mortality. If you stepped up to the altar and went to the far back, past the two giant brass Buddhas, you'd find around fifty large plastic containers, each holding the bones and ashes of one of the members of our congregation.

As I've mentioned, our monastery was also located in a cremation grove, which meant it hosted all local funeral services. At first, the mood at these funerals surprised me. They were so relaxed, people mingled, laughed and drank a lot of fizzy drinks. The only time I saw someone openly crying was when the deceased was a child.

The funerals went like this: in the afternoon, the relatives of the dead would push a wooden cart with the coffin from the village, singing all the way. The coffin was placed on a pyre and the body inside it was rotated so that it lay on its side. That was important because, if overlooked, the upper body of the deceased sometimes rose out of the coffin when the wood caught fire. I'm told it has something to do with the tendons.

Since tradition dictates that the deceased lie in an open coffin in his or her living room at home for three days before cremation, everyone's already getting used to the fact that the departed has gone. It's worth adding that the natural decomposition tropical heat triggers in an unrefrigerated body also helps to make death very concrete and not abstract in the slightest.

Sometimes I chose to spend all night next to the fire and the body burning in it, meditating on the impermanence of life and the inevitability of death. These meditations always calmed something restless inside me. They soothed something anxious. I softened, opened up and sort of cooled off inside, in the most pleasant sense of that phrase. It was as though my body recognised the truth when it saw it. And an uncomfortable truth does us good, so long as we stop turning away from it.

When I was younger, I spent quite a lot of time worrying about various aspects of my physical appearance. I complained about all the things that didn't look the way I wanted them to look. But today we have a very different relationship, my body and I. It feels more like an old friend. We've stuck together through thick and thin for a long time now. Neither one of us is young anymore. And I feel a lot of gratitude. I want to honour my body:

Thank you, body, for doing your best, all the time, every day.

You're fighting an uphill battle now. I see you.

You get absolutely nothing for free anymore. And yet, you do everything you can for me.

Even though you can't even get the air you need.

I'm doing everything I can to help you. And I can see it's not enough. Not nearly.

And yet, you fight on, giving it everything you have, day after day.

You're my hero.

I promise never to be angry with you again when yet another movement becomes impossible for you.

I promise to listen more and better to you than I ever have before.

I promise not to ask more of you than you can and want to give.

I'm sorry for all the times I did just that.

Last, and most important. I solemnly swear that when you can't go on any longer, we'll do what you want.

When that time comes, I'm going to do everything I can just to surrender and be grateful. To rest in trust and acceptance. To take joy from the amazing life we've had, and to whisper to you with a steady and undaunted voice:

'Thy will be done, not mine.'

THIRTY-FOUR

Be the thing you want to see more of in the world

My first abbot in Thailand, Ajahn Passano, didn't have the gift of eloquence. He didn't like giving lectures at all. He did it because it was expected of a person in his position. But the beautiful thing about him was to watch him move through his day. To see the way he made time for everyone who came within his sphere, the way he had enough patience for each of them. Some of his visitors were quite arrogant and wanted to brag about their spiritual state and, to their own minds, their success. Some were downright unpleasant. But Ajahn Passano treated everyone kindly and fairly. Being the abbot of a Buddhist monastery and a role model to all of us is certainly no easy task. But to me, he really was. He practised what he preached, could back up all his lessons with his own actions. His heart was always in the right place.

One night, during tea, Ajahn Passano started philosophising aloud to the rest of us. This was the same day my mum asked him how long it had been before he had visited his family in Canada, so that was probably what had brought this particular memory to mind. He started to describe the first time he went home in sixteen years:

It was Christmas and he was at his parents' house. His family and relatives had gathered for the holidays. Late one night, Ajahn Passano was sitting at a table with his cousin, who was drinking whisky. After a while, he poured a second glass and pushed it towards the monk's side of the table.

'Want one?'

'No, thank you. Monks and nuns in our tradition refrain from drinking alcohol.'

'Oh, come on,' the cousin coaxed, 'no one will even know.'

Ajahn Passano looked up at him and replied quietly and honestly:

'I will know.'

I remember the hairs on the back of my neck standing up when he said that. For me, a message sometimes carries extra weight when it comes from someone I feel safe with, whom I trust and respect. Such people can say relatively simple things that end up cutting straight to my core because I have faith in the source. For me Ajahn

Passano was one of those people. That's why this became such an inspirational moment and the most beautiful reminder I've ever had about why it's worth living a life of integrity. *That's* how I want to use ethics. *That's* how I want to take responsibility for my actions and words.

The reason I want to live with my back straight, guided by a sound moral compass, isn't because some book somewhere says I should. Or because some dusty old religious tract declares I ought to. It's not because I want to seem upstanding to others. Not because some silver-haired old man enthroned in clouds is judging everything we do and say. It's because I remember!

The things I'm ashamed about, the things I'm afraid people might find out, that's when I know I did something wrong – *that* is heavy baggage. It's so tedious to drag around. Imagine instead journeying through this life without too many shadows, without too many painful memories of times we didn't act in a dignified way.

That's why there's value in not deceiving others for our own gain, in not hurting others because it serves our purposes at the time, in avoiding bending or twisting the truth because it's more convenient.

All these things are human. Doing them comes easily most of the time. But something beautiful starts to happen when we actively choose to take responsibility for what we say and do. It lightens the load. We do it not just for others, but mostly for ourselves.

In Thailand, there's a lovely expression: they talk about 'gilding the Buddha's back'. It derives from the tradition of regularly going to the temple with a piece of gold leaf, candles and incense, to meditate for a while and then handing over those gifts to show your respect for your religion. Most Buddha statues in Thailand are covered in gold leaf. The expression means you don't have to advertise your good deeds. There's something delightful about the notion of placing your gold leaf on the Buddha's back, where no one will see it. Not least figuratively. It's not important that anyone else knows – you know. And you have to live with yourself all the time. Our actions and our memories are like the bathwater we sit in. It's up to us if it's clean or dirty.

We can discuss endlessly what's ethically and morally right. Philosophers have pondered these things for millennia. But, for me, it boils down to one simple fact: I have a conscience, I remember what I've done and said. Those things constitute my baggage. And I can choose what to pack.

So what are we responsible for in the ethical realm? Not impulses, that much is clear. We all have crazy impulses from time to time, hard as we may pretend we don't. Our abbot once told us about an incident during an American presidential election in the 1970s, which illustrates this pretty well. Jimmy Carter was well placed to become the next president. In an interview, a journalist asked him: 'Have you ever committed adultery?' Jimmy Carter replied: 'Never with my body, but many times in my imagination.' Confidence in him plummeted. But, as our teacher told us: had that interview taken place in a more enlightened culture, confidence in him would have increased instead. Because what could be more human? We can all relate. Impulses are primitive, ingrained behaviours we're not responsible for.

It's certainly nice, on the other hand, to see a person with enough maturity to practise good impulse control. A person who can pick and choose which impulses to act on and which to let go.

The Buddha put it best: a person who takes responsibility for his or her actions and words, who sticks to the truth, respects the rules, who doesn't deliberately hurt another; that person is like the full moon on a tropical night, slowly emerging from behind the clouds to light up the entire landscape.

When I was young, I watched a western called *Little Big Man*. In the film, there was an Indian chieftain, Old Lodge Skins. He has lived a hard life and one morning he comes out of his tepee and declares: '*Today is a good day to die.*' That's how I want death to come. Like a friend. You're welcome here, Death. You give me perspective and proportion by whispering in my ear: '*It all ends one day. Make sure you don't leave any shadows behind.*'

Because, suddenly, life ends. And then it will matter how I chose to live it. Whether or not we believe in karma, our baggage will in all likelihood affect how we feel – about what has been, what is and what may await us.

It's no coincidence all spiritual traditions emphasise the importance of remembering that we're all going to die one day. It's worth bearing that in mind when you make decisions and navigate your way through life. We can choose to bring out what's beautiful in ourselves. A little bit more today than yesterday. And even more tomorrow. Human life is short. When we truly under-stand that, when we stop taking each other and what we have for granted, then we move through our own lives differently.

We can't affect all possible outcomes or make every-thing come together exactly the way we want. But we can choose to act from our brightest intentions. We can take responsibility for the moral quality of our actions and our words. That's no small thing. It matters a great deal. And we can all do it. No one else needs to change for you to become more beautiful inside. It really is that simple.

I would guess an average ten-year-old is more or less able to spell out what's beautiful in the human heart. Patience, generosity, helpfulness, honesty, presence, the ability to forgive, the ability to put yourself in someone else's shoes for a while, empathy, listening, compassion, understanding, thoughtfulness. Identifying those qualities isn't hard. But I have a feeling our culture doesn't always encourage us to bring them out. That's why I want to highlight them. As a reminder to live life with our backs straight, to bring out what's most beautiful in us, while we can. I can't think of anything the world needs more right now.

Does that mean we have to fix all of humanity and solve every global problem? Do we all have to become a Greta Thunberg or a Gandhi? Absolutely not. A small minority just seem to have that in them. They like acting on that grand scale. And that's beautiful, that's good. But choosing to act in your own, immediate reality is just as valuable. To be mindful of everyday gestures. The miracle of the little things. When we choose to be a little more patient, forgiving, generous, honest and supportive than what might have been most convenient or easy for ourselves. Life really only consists of the little things, and, put together, they become the big things.

Every individual human life contains enough challenges. Each and every one of us faces crossroads every day: should I take the convenient route or the generous, beautiful, inclusive and caring one? In the long run, the two paths lead to vastly different destinations.

Life becomes both easier and freer when we're mindful of our internal moral compass; I often see proof of this.

We don't live in a random, indifferent universe. Quite the opposite. There's a resonance in this existence. The universe responds to the intentions behind what we do and say. What we send out eventually comes back. The world is not as it is. The world is as *you* are. So be what you want to see in it.

One story that has stuck with me is about a little girl walking along a beach. It's the morning after a stormy night, and the waves have washed up countless starfish. The little girl picks up a starfish and throws it back into the sea. Picks up another and throws it in, too. Then an old man comes along. A grumpy old man.

'Little girl, what are you doing?'

'I'm rescuing starfish by throwing them back into the water.'

'But, child, there must be tens if not hundreds of thousands of starfish on this beach. The few you throw back make absolutely no difference, you see that, don't you?'

Undeterred, the little girl picks up another starfish. Throws it in. And says:

'It matters to that one.'

After seventeen years as a monk, I had almost two decades of popular culture to catch up on – books to read, films and TV shows to watch – and I've made some brave attempts to do so. One TV show I'm particularly fond of, though it's relatively recent, I suppose, is the Norwegian series *Skam*. It's a wonderful depiction of youth, entirely from the perspective of the teenagers themselves. The grown-ups are just a backdrop, their faces rarely even seen on screen.

One of the show's most brilliant characters is called Noora. Beautiful as she is on the outside, she's even lovelier on the inside; I'm fairly taken with her. I would describe her as the friend many of us dream of having, and some of us may even have been lucky enough to have had. The friend who always backs you up, who's always on your side. The friend who's prepared to step far, far outside their comfort zone just to help you. The friend you trust so implicitly, because there's so much loving history between you, that she can say the things you need to hear, even when you don't want to hear them.

In one scene, Noora's blow-drying her hair, and to the left of the mirror we see a Post-it Note. It reads:

Everyone you meet
is fighting a battle
you know nothing about
Be kind
Always

Dad

My visit to the hospital in Varberg on that rainy day in September 2018 wasn't the first time Death put a bony finger on my shoulder. In fact, it had done so just a few months earlier, on a sunny afternoon in early June, at Mum and Dad's summer house in Falsterbo. They always make me feel like I'm the one person in the entire world they most wanted to step through their door. This day was no different. But after the hugs, I noticed a sombreness in the air. Dad said: 'Björn, there's something we need to tell you. Let's sit down.' We sat and Dad was as direct as usual: 'I have COPD. The clock is ticking. I probably don't have long to live.'

He said it completely without drama. Then he fell silent. I felt it was my turn to speak. At the same time, a storm had broken out inside me. It was important for me to say something sensible. After a moment of intense thought, I replied: '*You had a good run.*' After all, Dad was in his eighty-fourth year. He slapped his knee and said: 'I knew you'd get it!' Then he went on: 'And Björn, one more thing. I don't want to die a slow and painful death in hospital. I want to end things before the disease does it for me.'

That didn't sound as strange to me as you might think, because Dad had been saying the same thing for twenty years. If one day his life no longer felt worth living, he claimed the right to end it. During my years as a monk, I was unable to support his position because of the rules guiding monastic life. Monks and nuns are not allowed to encourage people to take their own lives under any circumstances. But now I felt differently.

Because assisted suicide is illegal in Sweden and time was short, my brothers and I immediately set to work to help Dad have it his way. We found an organisation in Switzerland, and by the end of the month we'd been given a date: on 26 July, Dad was going to die a pain-free, doctor-assisted death in Basel. Having an actual date was obviously very strange. Never had time felt more limited. The summer of 2018 was not only the hottest I can remember, but also the saddest. My grief counsellor that summer was called Spotify.

We were bringing speakers to Basel, and made playlists full of Evert Taube and Scottish bagpipes to fill Dad's last moments. My time for grieving was the early, early morning, while the world was still asleep. I often sat alone in front of my computer, preparing for our departure to Switzerland. From time to time I'd take a break from juggling medical documents, passport copies, bank business, flight and hotel booking and just listen to a song or two from our playlists for Dad. I still can't hear 'Amazing Grace' played on the bagpipe without losing it. Neither could Dad.

Eventually, the day arrived. We gathered at our hotel in Switzerland: Mum, Dad, my three brothers and I. Basel was even hotter than Sweden. As we had been doing for the past month and a half, we continued to move between realities together. Moments of mirth, playful ribbing and nostalgia alternated with moments when what lay ahead crept so close that words failed us. In those moments, looks spoke louder than words anyway. When Dad talked, he focused more than usual on expressing his appreciation and gratitude.

A taxi picked us up after breakfast and brought us to the outskirts of Basel and a pleasant room with a bed in the middle of it. The doctor walked us through what was going to happen. Dad lay down in the bed and an IV was put in his arm. Then the doctor left the room to give us some privacy.

We turned on the music we had prepared. Sven-Bertil Taube's voice filled the room. I don't think any of us realised we had so many tears left after a month of grieving. How wrong we were. I noticed that we took turns crying. Whoever needed a shoulder to cry on was given one, and, when they calmed down, they'd look around to see if they could do the same for someone else in turn. We filled a regular-sized bin with tissues in less than an hour. Dad was definitely the most collected.

He and I always had very different ideas of what happens after you die. Dad was convinced everything just goes black, curtain, and then nothing. So when I hugged him for the last time, I obviously whispered in his ear: 'Dad, if you do discover there's something else after this, make sure you imagine me saying: I told you so.' He laughed.

Everyone had a last moment with Dad. Mum said goodbye with a big bouquet of yellow roses, Dad's favourite flowers. After sixty years of unwavering love, there was little they needed to say to each other. I'll never forget the way they looked at each other when they thanked each other for everything. With love, of course, but also with a kind of respect I've had the enormous privilege of seeing between them my entire life. It's like they've never taken each other for granted.

When it was time to ask the doctor to come back in, I felt we were as ready as anyone can be to face an impossible moment. We'd had a month to say goodbye and everything else we wanted to tell each other. We sat around Dad's bed, holding onto each other, holding onto him. The doctor stood behind the IV stand. Dad looked each of us in the eyes, one by one.

Then he opened the line.

We'd been told it would take thirty to forty seconds for him to die. Two minutes passed. Then Dad turned to the doctor and said: 'Hey, Christian, are you sure you put the right stuff in that IV?'

We all laughed, of course.

Then something intense entered Dad's eyes. He turned to me and my three brothers and spoke his last words. A loving admonition that was so very him. I don't think any of us will ever forget those words.

A few seconds later, in the middle of Evert Taube's 'Linnéa', every muscle in Dad's body stopped working simultaneously. Death was instantaneous. I noticed an unexpected expression on Dad's gentle, open face. Total wonder. Like a child. As though he hadn't imagined in his wildest dreams that this was what happens when you die.

The first few moments after Dad passed away, it was like life itself held its breath. Everything just stopped. The doctor left the room and we looked at Dad, and at each other. No one really knew what to say. It was such a solemn moment. Words felt paltry. Eventually, someone closed Dad's eyes. Mum tenderly smoothed down his unruly eyebrows. Several of us patted him through the blanket. The light in the room was intensely yellow, from the roses, the wallpaper, the curtains and the sun in the sky outside.

Everything that had become so difficult for Dad – his breathing, his cough, his weakness – was over now. He had done it his way.

Gradually, we started talking, as though a spell were slowly lifting. I've never talked to my family about this, but it seemed to me Dad's spirit left him about half an hour after he died. It was very specific, and after that moment only his body was left.

Our dad, Mum's life partner, was no longer with us.

Eventually, Mum and my brothers went back into Basel. I had offered to stay behind. One of us had to, and since I'd spent my last two years as a monk in Switzerland, my German was at least functional.

Once I was alone with Dad's body, I lit a candle, bowed three times and then started to sing blessings. I sang the hymns I'd grown to love as a Buddhist monk, and that I had sung for hundreds of dead bodies together with my monk and nun friends to ease the passing of their souls. I had, of course, asked Dad's permission to do this before he died. At the same time, blessings were being sung for Dad in eight or nine Buddhist monasteries on four continents.

Then I meditated for a while, focusing both on aiding Dad's passage to the beyond and on reminding myself that my body – like everyone else's – would one day meet the same fate as Dad's. And that none of us knows how much time is left in our hourglass.

THIRTY-SIX

Forgiveness

We probably need to meet Death up close to truly understand that we won't have each other forever. On an intellectual level we're well aware of it, of course, the fact that we're all going to die one day. But it's the work of a lifetime to allow that knowledge and insight to sink down from our brains to the rest of us. And it's worth the effort.

Because what happens when we stop taking life for granted? What happens when we genuinely, with our entire being, understand that we don't have each other forever? We no longer have time for half-measures. One day, we're going to have to say goodbye – to every single person who means something to us. That we don't have each other forever is the only thing we know for sure. Everything else is a *maybe*. And when we bear that in mind, we realise there's only one way to approach other people and life itself: gently.

Is there anyone who needs to hear an 'I'm sorry' from you? Don't wait.

Is there anyone who needs to hear a few words only you can tell them the way they need to hear them to really listen? Don't hold back.

Is there anything you regret, that you can put right? Do it.

Maybe you have something in your life you feel you can't forgive? Sometimes, that's just how it is. But sometimes, it can also be helpful to try this thought: if you'd been born with the same DNA, the same karma, the same codes as them, if you'd grown up exactly the same way, with the same people around you, been through the same things they have, then you would probably have acted exactly like them.

I'm not denying there's evil in this world that passes understanding. But that's not what I'm talking about now. Even in our 'regular' lives, we encounter mean and callous acts that deserve utter condemnation. We can condemn those acts. But we don't have to close our hearts to the person who committed them. It is a mark of how far we've come when we have genuinely learned to separate people from their actions. Being interested in growing in love, simply because it feels beautiful to want to meet everyone and everything with warmth, doesn't make you a wimp. You're still perfectly capable of putting your foot down when someone goes too far, acts in bad faith. But you can separate the deed and the person.

Does me saying this strike a nerve with you? Is there maybe someone in your life you've been refusing to let back into your heart? That's eminently understandable. Reconciliation and forgiveness are not easy things. But please try to assess the effects of your feelings objectively and with a level head. What happens when you close your heart to someone? *That person* may not be visibly harmed, but *you* are. It makes you a little bit smaller. You're planting seeds of bitterness inside yourself. And if you choose to remind yourself frequently about this person you can't forgive, that can let that bitterness grow to the point where it does you real harm, without punishing the other person one bit.

I've always been fascinated by the Japanese soldiers in the Pacific who refused to believe the Second World War was over. Some remained at their posts for decades after peace was restored, with their weapons at the ready. They weren't going to let anyone trick them into thinking the war was over, *nothing* could make them surrender!

We're often like that ourselves. We're so focused on the battle that we miss the white flags. But in the end, we realise – *the war is over*. It's been over for a long time. And the peace we make with ourselves is the most important of all. Once we get there, so many things fall into place, naturally and of their own accord.

I love that image: *The war is over. Run up the white flag.* This is the only place reconciliation can begin. We can't wait for someone else to be ready to forgive, reconcile and move on.

This is where it begins. This is where it ends.

I have a memory from my early years as a monk that I think about from time to time. An incident that gave me a clear example of the mechanisms of letting go of injustices.

Every year in January we celebrated the memory of Ajahn Chah, the founder of our monastery and a very important monk within the forest tradition. We celebrated the great master's passing by observing the day of his death as tradition dictates. He died just twelve days after I first arrived at the monastery. This ceremony was spread and established all over the world, and every year monks and nuns came from different countries to mark the occasion with us. A regular participant was a senior monk from England. He was someone we all found difficult to be around. So as the time of his visit drew near, our teacher told us something along the lines of: 'All right. Let's make sure we give this monk the five-star treatment. The few short days he's with us we're going to make him feel like a beloved master.'

That felt like a beautiful sentiment and it resonated with us. Here comes someone who has some difficulty getting monks to stay with him, who is slightly difficult to live with, an eccentric. Let's do our best. So we did.

One night, I was sitting with the senior monk outside his hut, massaging his feet. The massage culture was strong within our tradition and we often rubbed each other's feet. Mainly, younger monks massaged the feet of their elders. It was like an excuse to hang out with them and listen to their stories and pearls of wisdom. Westerners usually felt awkward about it at first, but for the Thai, who live in a much more physical culture, it seemed more natural.

I've been told that Ajahn Chah, who was Thai, once asked a senior monk from the West, Ajahn Sumedho, if he used to rub his father's feet. Ajahn Sumedho, who's American and was born in 1934, replied with revulsion: 'Certainly not!' And Ajahn Chah calmly retorted: 'Maybe that's why you have so many problems.'

So I sat there, with my small piece of cloth, a bottle of oil and the wooden massage wand I'd made myself (for use on feet only!). And we were having a nice time, in the usual way of monks. The English monk began to tell me about the good old days, about the masters he'd met and the adventures he'd experienced. It was all very pleasant. Then a name was mentioned. The name of another senior monk in our tradition. The English monk's demeanour changed completely. Suddenly, he was very angry, curt, indignant and bitter. He started telling me about all the things this monk had done wrong a long time ago and how unfair it all was. Young and naive as I was, I said something like, 'Okay, but still, that was twenty-two years ago, isn't it time to let it go?'

Let me give you a piece of advice: never tell a person who's upset to let it go. It rarely lands well, and just as rarely has the desired effect. The only person we should tell to let things go is ourselves, that's the only time it works. But I hadn't yet learned that lesson. My words didn't have the intended effect. The bitter monk was not a quantum less bitter. Possibly slightly *more*.

After leaving his hut, I spent some time pondering what had really happened. I think the angry monk reminded himself of those injustices, those *perceived* injustices, perpetrated against him virtually daily and by reminding himself so often he kept the memory fresh, as though it had happened the day before yesterday. His bitterness was, if you like, 'online' – accessible every hour of the day, seven days a week.

There's one thing worth noting here. It explains how forgiveness can be a key to freedom. Reconciling ourselves to what has happened isn't mainly about being the bigger person. It's about protecting our own mental wellbeing, about choosing which feelings to fill our minds with.

One of my favourites in the forest tradition was the Thai monk Luang Por Doon. He was very intelligent and at the same time deeply meditatively experienced. The

Thai king and queen at the time were his disciples, so they regularly travelled to see Luang Por Doon to give him gifts and ask questions. On one occasion, the king respectfully asked: 'Luang Por Doon, do You ever get angry?' It was a sensitive subject, because in eastern religions equanimity is held to be very important. It's considered admirable not to let yourself get swept up in strong emotions and reactions. Luang Por Doon replied in Thai: 'Mee, date mai aow.' It means something like: 'Anger arises, but nothing does it occupy.'

I like this story because it illustrates what life can be like when our inner space is big enough to contain all our feelings. It's not that we stop having those feelings we view as negative or difficult. We just stop identifying with them; we don't let them occupy us. Then, they can no longer harm us, or make us do things we regret.

From shallowness to sincerity

Sometimes, when people hear my story, they say something like, 'Imagine, all the things you must have learned!' Maybe I have, but I don't feel like I'm toting around a big sack full of timeless wisdom. Almost the exact opposite. I travel through life with less baggage than ever. Less of me and more room for life. It has made me wiser, but more like Winnie-the-Pooh than Rabbit. These days, awareness is the only thing I trust when life turns stormy. As often as I can, I let go of my resistance to feeling the hard feelings. I try to welcome them instead, breathe through them, become a bit more like the Moominpappa when he gazes out at the sea and says: 'There's a storm coming, kids. Come on, let's take the boat out!'

Slowly but surely, I've come to understand that there's a wiser voice I can listen to, that I can dance with life instead of trying to control it. That I can live my life with an open hand rather than a fist clenched in fear. I really don't want to give anyone the impression that you have to go and live as a monk or nun for seventeen years to get access to the kind of wisdom I'm talking about. We all have it much closer to hand than that. In Hinduism, there's a saying: *God hid the most precious of all jewels where he knew you would never look for it: in your own pocket.*

I had a wonderful reminder of this one night in the monastery in Thailand. After our evening meditation, Ajahn Jayasaro decided to give a spontaneous lecture, as he liked to do once or twice a week. This particular evening, he told us about a BBC interview with the Thai king. The British journalist had asked the king what he thought of the western, Christian idea of original sin. And the king's answer was lovely:

'As Buddhists, we do not believe in original sin. We believe in original purity.'

I shuddered on my meditation cushion when I heard that. What if that voice inside me, the one that had so often whispered I wasn't good enough, was actually wrong?

What if, instead, it's true what so many spiritual and religious traditions have always maintained: that the core – the indestructible part – of a person is completely innocent and unproblematic. Always has been, always will be.

THIRTY-EIGHT

This is where it ends

As this book is being written, the corona pandemic is raging in Sweden and large parts of the world. Given my illness, complete isolation is obviously the order of the day. One of the upsides of quarantine is that I've started to FaceTime once a fortnight with my best monk friend Ajahn Sucitto in England. The other day, he read me a South African short story. The final scene consisted of a touching gesture of generosity between two complete strangers.

Since Ajahn Sucitto happens to have one of the biggest hearts of anyone I've ever had the honour of knowing, the story really moved me. Through my tears, I managed to say something along the lines of: 'These days, gestures like that feel like the only things that matter!'

Ajahn Sucitto replied calmly: 'Not nowadays. Always. It's just that some superficial fluff has been stripped away by the pandemic, making it that much more obvious.'

In my situation, that question takes on extra urgency, of course: *What's important, truly important, to me now?*

It has become less important to please others. Before, that was always more important to me than I wanted it to be.

It has become more important to express my gratitude. Because most people are like me: they don't appreciate how appreciated they really are.

It has become more important than ever to live right here right now in every moment, instead of getting lost in thoughts about what things should be like or what might be.

My circle has shrunk. I focus more on the people closest to me. I want to make absolutely sure they know how fond I am of them.

Play has become increasingly important. Having opinions has become less important. I love the reply Ajahn Chah – the legendary Thai forest monk – gave when he was asked: 'What is the biggest obstacle on the road to enlightenment for your western disciples?' Insightfully, in a single word, he replied: 'Opinions'.

Being a good friend to myself has never been more important. This is when the going gets tough. It's time to listen gently to myself. Speak kindly to myself. Afford myself as much patience as I give others on a good day. Approach myself with more humour.

It's important to me to meditate with Elisabeth every morning. To let go of my thoughts breath by breath and instead slowly lean back into that which was inside me before I was born, and which will endure when the rest of me dies.

For me, it's like something I've longed for all my life, without knowing what it was. As though someone, for as long as I can remember, has been sitting on my shoulder, whispering: 'Come home!'

So how does one find the way back home? The best answer to that question I've come across so far comes from Meister Eckhart, a German priest in the early fourteenth century, who was supposedly enlightened. After a Sunday sermon, an elderly member of his congregation came up to him and said: 'Meister Eckhart, You have clearly met God. Please help me get to know God like You do. But Your advice must be short and simple, my memory is failing me.'

'It's very simple,' Meister Eckhart replied. 'All you need to do to meet God the way I have is to fully understand who is looking out through your eyes.'

Just a few years into my life as a Buddhist monk, I was doing a walking meditation one afternoon on the meditation path outside my bamboo hut in the jungle. At the same time, I was listening to a lecture by a monk called Ajahn Brahm. He was talking about death, and at one point he said: 'When my time comes, I hope it will feel like stepping out into the cool night air, happy and dazed like after an amazing Led Zeppelin concert.' I knew exactly what he meant. Now that I, sooner than I had hoped, perhaps, am approaching my last breath, it is with a similar feeling. Thankfully, I can look back at my life without an ounce of regret or anxiety, and with an irresistible mix of astonishment and gratefulness say:

Wow, what a ride, what an adventure I've had! Who would have thought?! How is it that I've experienced so much? I feel like I've lived three lives in one lifetime.

How is it that I always find myself in the company of wiser people with bigger hearts than myself?

How is it that things haven't ended badly for me more often, considering the many shockingly rash and sometimes undeniably dangerous things I've done?

Why on earth do so many people like me so much?

How can things have turned out so well for me when I never had much of a plan?

There was a wise, lovable monk once by the name of Luang Por Jun. Towards the end of his long life, he was diagnosed with a particularly pernicious form of liver cancer. His chances of survival were minimal. That notwithstanding, his doctor presented him with a long and complex treatment plan that involved radiation, chemotherapy and surgery. When the doctor had finished, Luang Por Jun turned his warm, unafraid eyes to his monk friend who had come with him and said: '*Don't doctors die?*'

I heard the story after the fact, and it has stayed with me. It struck a chord.

Why is the dominant narrative in our culture as far as facing death is concerned this heroic tale of fighting, resisting and denying? Why is death so often painted as an enemy to be defeated? As an insult or a failure? I don't like to think of death as the opposite of life. More like the opposite of birth. And I obviously can't prove it, but I've always had an innate conviction that there's something on the other side. Sometimes, I even feel like a marvellous adventure is waiting for me.

The day my last breath comes – whenever that may be – please, don't ask me to fight it. Instead, do everything you can to help me to let go. Tell me you'll be fine and that you'll stick together. Help me to remember everything we have to be grateful for. Show me your open hands, so I remember what I want it to feel like when it's time.

Elisabeth, if you're not already in my bed then, crawl in with me and hold me. Look me in the eyes. I want the last thing I see in this life to be your eyes.

Acknowledgements

Given the circumstances, you could be excused for thinking I've written a book. I really like the idea of being a person who has written a book. The actual book writing, on the other hand, I seem less fond of.

In a show of faith, Bonnier offered me a book deal in 2011, and then another in 2016. But writer's block and perfectionism proved formidable opponents and both times I was overcome.

Unwilling to admit defeat, however, Bonnier sent their most persistent scout and tracker, Martin Ransgart, to flush me out. I was in the middle of my tour 'The Keys to Freedom' and had given up on ever writing a book. But Martin was relentless. He popped up like a jack-in-the-box in lecture halls, at film premiers, via text, phone calls, email and Facebook messenger. In the end, I felt that kind of persistence had to be rewarded, so I said yes. But I made it clear I was going to need help.

This book owes more to my touring partner, Caroline Bankler, than anyone else. With her linguistic brilliance and intuitive grasp of how I express myself, she wrote an entire book in the first person singular, unreasonably quickly and unbelievably deftly. Then my podcasting partner Navid Modiri made the book even more entertaining and improved the reading experience by moving certain sections and headers around. Then Caroline and I suggested some additional changes to preserve the book's distinctiveness. Bonnier's editor Ingemar E. Nilsson proved invaluable to the editing process, generously sharing his considerable competence, creativity and human warmth. Linus Lindgren did a lot of the heavy lifting by curating and transcribing my words from countless podcasts, lectures, guided meditations and two appearances on Sveriges radio's *Sommar*.

So I still haven't written a book. Caroline has written a book. Navid, Ingemar, Martin, Linus, and I just assisted her to the best of our abilities.

My hope is that the book speaks for itself, that it speaks to you. That you choose to come back to it from time to time. That certain passages and ideas in it become your companions in life. That the book can be a friend that entertains and stimulates when all is well, and comforts and restores your faith when circumstances are more challenging.

Thank you having faith in me.

With unbroken warmth,

Björn Natthiko Lindeblad

Thank you, Mum, Emma, Malin, Victor, Johan, Johanna and above all you, my darling Fredrik! You know why. Thank you also to Martin for your relentless persistence, to Ingemar for your infinite patience, and to Navid for your tireless conviction that everything will turn out all right in the end. Among other things. Last and most of all – thank you Björn for the greatest gift of faith and trust I have ever been given. And for everything along the way. You rock my world.

Caroline

Thank you, Björn, for your wisdom, your trust, and for being one of the most distinctive people I've ever had the pleasure of playing with. Thank you, Caroline, for your steadiness, incomparable diligence, and uncompromising eye for quality. Thank you, Martin, Ingemar, and everyone at Bonnier. Thank you, Linus, for your enormous dedication and the countless hours of transcribing, listening and patience. Thank you, Amy, Howard, and Adyashanti for your support and encouraging words on this journey.

Navid

A Note on the Author

Björn Natthiko Lindeblad (born 1961) is a Swedish public speaker, meditation teacher and former Buddhist monk. In his mid-twenties Björn swapped his career as a business executive for life as a forest monk in the jungles of Thailand. There he was given the name Natthiko, meaning 'one who grows in wisdom'. After seventeen years as a monk he returned to Swedish society and, in 2018, was diagnosed with the incurable disease ALS. I May Be Wrong, his first book, was an instant number one bestseller in Sweden, and won both the Adilibris and Storytel Awards for Best Non-Fiction.

A Note on the Type

The text of this book is set in Joanna, a transitional serif typeface designed by Eric Gill (1882–1940) in the period 1930–31, and named for one of his daughters. The typeface was originally designed for proprietary use by Gill's printing shop, Hague & Gill. The type was first produced in a small quantity by the Caslon Foundry for hand composition. It was eventually licensed for public release by the Monotype foundry in 1937.